Collins Primary Maths
Answer Book

Series Editor: Peter Clarke

Authors: Andrew Edmondson, Elizabeth Jurgensen,
Jeanette Mumford, Sandra Roberts

Published by Collins Educational
An imprint of HarperCollins*Publishers* Ltd
77–85 Fulham Palace Road
Hammersmith
London
W6 8JB
www.**Collins**Education.com
On-line support for schools and colleges

First published 2000

10 9 8 7 6 5

© HarperCollins*Publishers* Ltd

All rights reserved. No part of this publication may be reproduced,
stored in a retrieval system or transmitted in any form or by any
means – electronic, mechanical, photocopying, recording or otherwise
– without either the prior written permission of the Publisher or a
licence permitting restricted copying in the United Kingdom issued by
the Copyright Licencing Agency Ltd, 90 Tottenham Court Road,
London W1P OLP.

ISBN 000 315 3088

Cover design by Susi Martin and Jacqueline Palmer

Cover illustration by Jan Lewis

Series design by Sylvia Tate

Text page design by Ken Vail Graphic Design

Printed by Martins the Printers, Berwick

Contents

Collins Primary Maths

Answers

Pupil Book 1

Autonn wait

Autumn

Week 1, Lesson 1 – Pages 4 and 5

Practice

1 a 500 000   b 900   c 5 000
  d 20 000   e 4   f 3 000 000
  g 200   h 4 000 000   i 30 000

2 a five hundred and eighty-six thousand, two hundred and fourteen
  b seven hundred and twenty thousand, nine hundred and sixty-three
  c four hundred and sixty-five thousand, seven hundred and sixty-nine
  d three hundred and twenty-seven thousand, one hundred and twenty-five
  e nine hundred and two thousand, eight hundred and twenty-four
  f three million, six hundred and eighty-four thousand, nine hundred and seventy-seven
  g two million, nine hundred and sixty-two thousand, two hundred and five
  h four million, seventy-three thousand, six hundred and seventeen
  i eight million, eight hundred and thirty-one thousand, four hundred and twenty-nine

3 a $30 \times 10 = 300$
  b $45 \times 10 = 450$
  c $37 \times 100 = 3700$
  d $21 \times 1000 = 21\,000$
  e $86 \times 1000 = 86\,000$
  f $124 \times 100 = 12\,400$
  g $263 \times 10 = 2630$
  h $191 \times 100 = 19\,100$
  i $506 \times 1000 = 506\,000$
  j $712 \times 10 = 7120$
  k $6.2 \times 10 = 62$
  l $8.7 \times 100 = 870$
  m $19.4 \times 10 = 194$
  n $67.26 \times 100 = 6726$
  o $74.39 \times 10 = 743.9$

4 a $64\,000 \div 10 = 6400$
  b $7800 \div 100 = 78$
  c $8100 \div 10 = 810$
  d $9600 \div 100 = 96$
  e $58\,000 \div 100 = 580$
  f $42\,000 \div 1000 = 42$
  g $3000 \div 1000 = 3$
  h $6700 \div 1000 = 6.7$
  i $910 \div 100 = 9.1$
  j $863 \div 100 = 8.63$
  k $721 \div 10 = 72.1$
  l $578 \div 100 = 5.78$
  m $67 \div 10 = 6.7$
  n $28.3 \div 10 = 2.83$
  o $165 \div 100 = 1.65$

5 Children should explain that the place values of the digits change. When multiplying by 10, 100 or 1000, the place value of each digit moves 1, 2 or 3 places to the left. When dividing by 10, 100 or 1000, the place value of each digit moves 1, 2 or 3 places to the right.

Refresher

1 a 6000   b 20   c 100
  d 4   e 20 000   f 5000
  g 300   h 60 000   i 5

2 a six thousand, five hundred and eighty-one
  b nine thousand, one hundred and twenty-three
  c seven thousand, one hundred and sixty-four
  d three thousand, eight hundred and fifty-four
  e twenty-eight thousand, three hundred and sixty-one
  f thirty-five thousand, six hundred and eighty-four

Collins Primary Maths

g twenty-four thousand, three
   hundred and sixty-two
h sixty-two thousand, one hundred
   and forty-six
i seventy-eight thousand, two
   hundred and five

3 a $58 \times 10 = 580$ b $72 \times 10 = 720$
  c $61 \times 10 = 610$ d $94 \times 10 = 940$
  e $751 \times 10 = 7510$ f $361 \times 10 = 3610$
  g $821 \times 10 = 8210$ h $500 \times 10 = 5000$
  i $6200 \times 10 = 62000$
  j $5641 \times 10 = 56410$
  k $7013 \times 10 = 70130$
  l $5267 \times 10 = 52670$

4 a $90 \div 10 = 9$ b $20 \div 10 = 2$
  c $60 \div 10 = 6$ d $250 \div 10 = 25$
  e $170 \div 10 = 17$ f $800 \div 10 = 80$
  g $960 \div 10 = 96$ h $470 \div 10 = 47$
  i $2650 \div 10 = 265$ j $3820 \div 10 = 382$
  k $9800 \div 10 = 980$ l $7260 \div 10 = 726$

5 a $45 \times 100 = 4500$
  b $38 \times 100 = 3800$
  c $475 \times 100 = 47500$
  d $200 \times 100 = 20000$
  e $634 \times 100 = 63400$

6 a $400 \div 100 = 4$ b $600 \div 100 = 6$
  c $4500 \div 100 = 45$ d $3100 \div 100 = 31$
  e $40000 \div 100 = 400$

Challenge

1 13, 130, 1300
2 1450, 14500, 145000

Week 1, Lesson 2 – Pages 6 – 7

Practice

1	10	100	1000
a 73 140	73 100	73 000
b 62 270	62 300	62 000
c 15 510	15 500	16 000
d 27 820	27 800	28 000
e 49 080	49 100	49 000
f 487 270	487 300	487 000
g 931 860	931 900	932 000
h 518 960	519 000	519 000
i 297 030	297 000	297 000
j 499 760	499 800	500 000

2 a $\times 100$ b $\times 100$
  c $\times 1000$ d $\times 100$
  e $\times 100$ f $\div 1000$
  g $\div 100$ h $\div 1000$
  i $\div 1000$ j $\div 100$

3 For each operation, you end up with
  the number you started with.

Refresher

1	10	100	1000
a 1760	1800	2000
b 2490	2500	2000
c 3530	3500	4000
d 5090	5100	5000
e 7320	7300	7000
f 2380	2400	2000
g 4230	4200	4000
h 7570	7600	8000
i 5060	5100	5000
j 1920	1900	2000

2 a 6200   b 7600
  c 21 000   d 47 000
  e 23 000   f 4
  g 39   h 67.2
  i 8   j 7.2

3 Each operation comes back to the
  number you started with.

Challenge

1 a 1000   b 1000   c 100
  d 10 000 e 10   f 100 000

Week 1, Lesson 3 – Pages 8 and 9

Practice

1 a $-2\,°C$ b $7\,°C$
  c $-7\,°C$ d $-7\,°C$
  e $8\,°C$ f $15\,°C$
  g $12\,°C$ h $8\,°C$
  i $8\,°C$ j $4\,°C$

Refresher

1 a -10 -5 -4 -1 3 6 7 9
  b -14 -5 -3 -2 0 2 8 10
  c -21 -8 -7 -3 1 7 12 15
  d -9 -8 -4 -2 -1 0 3 5
  e -31 -29 -28 -25 -22 -15 -11 -6

2 a −1 °C   **b** −3 °C
c −4 °C   **d** −9 °C
e −3 °C   **f** −6 °C
g −4 °C   **h** −4 °C

Challenge

a $4 - 9 = -5$ **b** $3 - 15 = -12$
c $0 - 7 = -7$ **d** $2 - 12 = -10$
e $1 - 13 = -12$ **f** $-9 + 3 = -6$
g $-10 + 9 = -1$ **h** $-14 + 5 = -9$
i $-20 + 7 = -13$ **j** $-18 + 12 = -6$
k $-12 + 6 = -6$ **l** $0 - 12 = -12$

Week 2, Lesson 1 Pages 10 and 11

Practice

a £22
b £32
c No, it should be £35
d Gatwick
e £50
f 2 people to Stansted
g £18, £21, £28, £35
h £3 each
i £96
j £28, £56
k 2 taxis, one with 4 passengers and the other with 5 passengers
l 2 taxis with 3 passengers in each

Refresher

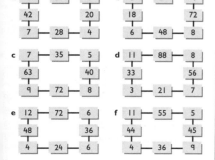

Challenge

1 The product of the numbers in each row, in each column and in both diagonals is the same.

3 a

28	49	2
1	14	196
98	4	7

b

32	4	4
1	8	64
16	16	2

Week 2, Lesson 2 – Pages 12 and 13

Practice

Double
$3.6 \times 2 = 7.2$
$9400 \times 2 = 18\,800$
$7800 \times 2 = 15\,600$
$960 \times 2 = 1920$
$41.2 \times 2 = 82.4$
$850 \times 2 = 1700$
$18.9 \times 2 = 37.8$
$6900 \times 2 = 13\,800$
$25.5 \times 2 = 51$
$740 \times 2 = 1480$
$8300 \times 2 = 16\,600$
$0.13 \times 2 = 0.26$
$4600 \times 2 = 9200$
$520 \times 2 = 1040$
$9900 \times 2 = 19\,800$

Halve
$\frac{1}{2} \times 24.6 = 12.3$
$\frac{1}{2} \times 12\,800 = 6400$
$\frac{1}{2} \times 48.8 = 24.4$

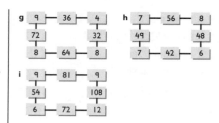

Collins Primary Maths

$\frac{1}{2} \times 1140 = 570$

$\frac{1}{2} \times 50.6 = 25.3$

$\frac{1}{2} \times 15400 = 7700$

$\frac{1}{2} \times 16900 = 8450$

$\frac{1}{2} \times 0.74 = 0.37$

$\frac{1}{2} \times 680 = 340$

$\frac{1}{2} \times 11300 = 5650$

$\frac{1}{2} \times 0.56 = 0.28$

$\frac{1}{2} \times 13600 = 6800$

$\frac{1}{2} \times 1540 = 770$

$\frac{1}{2} \times 5.8 = 2.9$

$\frac{1}{2} \times 11 = 5.5$

Refresher

a $18 \times 2 = 36$

$86 \times 2 = 172$

$45 \times 2 = 90$

$74 \times 2 = 148$

$53 \times 2 = 106$

b $\frac{1}{2} \times 92 = 46$

$\frac{1}{2} \times 30 = 15$

$\frac{1}{2} \times 64 = 32$

$\frac{1}{2} \times 26 = 13$

$\frac{1}{2} \times 52 = 26$

c $82 \times 2 = 164$

$37 \times 2 = 74$

$95 \times 2 = 190$

$29 \times 2 = 58$

$48 \times 2 = 96$

d $\frac{1}{2} \times 74 = 37$

$\frac{1}{2} \times 78 = 39$

$\frac{1}{2} \times 96 = 48$

$\frac{1}{2} \times 64 = 32$

$\frac{1}{2} \times 56 = 28$

e $39 \times 2 = 78$

$63 \times 2 = 126$

$25 \times 2 = 50$

$40 \times 2 = 80$

$45 \times 2 = 90$

f $98 \div 2 = 49$

$74 \div 2 = 37$

$62 \div 2 = 31$

Answers will vary

Challenge

Answers will vary

Week 2, Lesson 3 – Pages 14 and 15

Practice

1 a $17 \times 50 \rightarrow (17 \times 100) \div 2$

$\rightarrow 1700 \div 2$

$\rightarrow 850$

b $64 \times 50 = 3200$

c $32 \times 50 = 1600$

d $25 \times 50 = 1250$

e $28 \times 50 = 1400$

f $50 \times 50 = 2500$

g $82 \times 50 = 4100$

h $39 \times 50 = 1950$

i $76 \times 50 = 3800$

j $91 \times 50 = 4550$

2 a $16 \times 25 \rightarrow (16 \times 100) \div 4$

$\rightarrow 1600 \div 4$

$\rightarrow 400$

b $48 \times 25 = 1200$

c $32 \times 25 = 800$

d $24 \times 25 = 600$

e $44 \times 25 = 1100$

f $26 \times 25 = 650$

g $34 \times 25 = 850$

h $50 \times 25 = 1250$

i $60 \times 25 = 1500$

j $38 \times 25 = 950$

3 a $12 \times 25 = 300$

b $36 \times 25 = 900$

c $28 \times 25 = 700$

d $80 \times 25 = 2000$

e $30 \times 25 = 750$

f $52 \times 25 = 1300$

g $46 \times 25 = 1150$

h $77 \times 25 = 1925$

Refresher

1 a $23 \times 100 = 2300$

b $34 \times 100 = 3400$

c $62 \times 100 = 6200$

d $89 \times 100 = 8900$

e $17 \times 100 = 1700$

f $45 \times 100 = 4500$

g $56 \times 100 = 5600$

h $99 \times 100 = 9900$

i $100 \times 100 = 10000$

j $400 \times 100 = 40000$

k $421 \times 100 = 42100$

l $126 \times 100 = 12600$

m $243 \times 100 = 24300$

n $157 \times 100 = 15700$

o $318 \times 100 = 31800$

Challenge

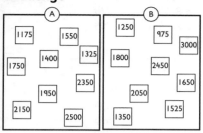

Week 2, Lesson 4 – Pages 16 and 17

Practice

1 a $8 \times 24 = (8 \times 6) \times 2 \times 2$
$= (48 \times 2) \times 2$
$= 96 \times 2$
$= 192$

b $12 \times 24 = 288$
c $20 \times 24 = 480$
d $9 \times 24 = 216$
e $15 \times 24 = 360$
f $24 \times 24 = 576$
g $32 \times 24 = 768$
h $30 \times 24 = 720$
i $50 \times 24 = 1200$
j $42 \times 24 = 1008$

2 a $6 \times 24 = \boxed{6} \xrightarrow{\times 6} \boxed{36} \xrightarrow{\text{double}} \boxed{72} \xrightarrow{\text{double}} \boxed{144}$

b $22 \times 24 = 528$
c $16 \times 24 = 384$
d $25 \times 24 = 600$
e $40 \times 24 = 960$
f $52 \times 24 = 1248$
g $35 \times 24 = 840$
h $60 \times 24 = 1440$
i $13 \times 24 = 312$

3 a

D	H
36	25
~~72~~	~~12~~
~~144~~	~~6~~
288	3
576	1
900	

$36 \times 25 = 900$

b $43 \times 24 = 1032$
c $24 \times 37 = 888$

Refresher

1 The number facts for the multiples of 6 are:

$12 \times 6 = 72$
$3 \times 6 = 18$
$11 \times 6 = 66$
$8 \times 6 = 48$
$7 \times 6 = 42$
$10 \times 6 = 60$
$5 \times 6 = 30$
$6 \times 6 = 36$
$4 \times 6 = 24$
$20 \times 6 = 120$
$2 \times 6 = 12$
$9 \times 6 = 54$

Challenge

1 Open
2 Open
3 a $46 \times 24 = 1104$
b $47 \times 28 = 1316$
c $26 \times 32 = 832$
4 Answers will vary

Week 2, Lesson 5 – Pages 18 and 19

Practice

1 a $7 \times 36 = 252$ **b** $4 \times 36 = 144$
c $5 \times 36 = 180$ **d** $3 \times 36 = 108$
e $6 \times 36 = 216$
2 a $8 \times 48 = 384$ **b** $4 \times 48 = 192$
c $9 \times 48 = 432$ **d** $3 \times 48 = 144$
e $5 \times 48 = 240$
3 a $5 \times 27 = 135$ **b** $3 \times 27 = 81$
c $7 \times 27 = 189$ **d** $6 \times 27 = 162$
e $9 \times 27 = 243$
4 a $8 \times 24 = 192$ **b** $5 \times 24 = 120$
c $3 \times 24 = 72$ **d** $7 \times 24 = 168$
e $6 \times 24 = 144$
5 a $4 \times 38 = 152$ **b** $8 \times 38 = 304$
c $3 \times 38 = 114$ **d** $7 \times 38 = 266$
e $6 \times 38 = 228$
6 a $9 \times 54 = 486$ **b** $5 \times 54 = 270$
c $6 \times 54 = 324$ **d** $4 \times 54 = 216$
e $8 \times 54 = 432$

Collins Primary Maths

7a $3 \times 63 = 189$ **b** $8 \times 63 = 504$
c $5 \times 63 = 315$ **d** $6 \times 63 = 378$
e $2 \times 63 = 126$
8a $7 \times 45 = 315$ **b** $4 \times 45 = 180$
c $3 \times 45 = 135$ **d** $5 \times 45 = 225$
e $8 \times 45 = 360$

Refresher

1 a $47 \times 3 = (40 \times 3) + (7 \times 3)$
$\qquad\qquad = 120 + 21$
$\qquad\qquad = 141$
b $44 \times 6 = 264$ **c** $76 \times 8 = 608$
d $36 \times 9 = 324$ **e** $53 \times 8 = 424$
f $78 \times 6 = 468$ **g** $65 \times 4 = 260$
h $48 \times 7 = 336$ **i** $93 \times 4 = 372$
j $86 \times 5 = 430$

Challenge

Jack
a $64 \times 6 = 384$ **b** $45 \times 3 = 135$
c $59 \times 4 = 236$ **d** $73 \times 7 = 511$
e $87 \times 8 = 696$ **f** $68 \times 9 = 612$
g $96 \times 5 = 480$

Sam
a $37 \times 4 = 148$ **b** $56 \times 7 = 392$
c $65 \times 9 = 585$ **d** $83 \times 5 = 415$
e $78 \times 3 = 234$ **f** $49 \times 8 = 392$
g $74 \times 6 = 444$

Week 3, Lesson 1 – Pages 20 and 21

Practice

1 a

3626×5	×	3000	600	20	6	= 18130
	5	15 000	3000	100	30	

b $6324 \times 3 = 18972$
c $2761 \times 4 = 11044$
d $8192 \times 9 = 73728$
e $5293 \times 8 = 42344$
f $1423 \times 3 = 4269$
g $5732 \times 5 = 28660$
h $4901 \times 4 = 19604$
i $6882 \times 9 = 61938$
j $9123 \times 4 = 36492$
k $6812 \times 3 = 20436$
l $8002 \times 5 = 40010$

m $4375 \times 6 = 26250$
n $8534 \times 7 = 59738$
o $2964 \times 6 = 17784$

2 a

1287×7	×	1000	200	80	7	= 9009
	7	7000	1400	560	49	

b $4032 \times 2 = 8064$
c $3504 \times 6 = 21024$
d $7123 \times 5 = 35615$
e $3875 \times 6 = 23250$
f $2081 \times 7 = 14567$
g $8160 \times 8 = 65280$
h $7214 \times 2 = 14428$
i $4190 \times 8 = 33520$
j $2102 \times 6 = 12612$
k $7575 \times 7 = 53025$
l $3761 \times 9 = 33849$
m $3052 \times 3 = 9156$
n $1359 \times 4 = 5436$
o $2658 \times 4 = 10632$

Refresher

1 a

326×8	×	300	20	6	= 2608
	8	2400	160	48	

b $124 \times 6 = 744$
c $641 \times 7 = 4487$
d $532 \times 4 = 2128$
e $375 \times 3 = 1125$
f $287 \times 9 = 2583$
g $704 \times 3 = 2112$
h $642 \times 5 = 3210$
i $493 \times 8 = 3944$

Challenge

1 a

7124×3	×	7000	100	20	4	= 21 372
	3	21 000	300	60	12	

b 4583   **c** 3426   **d** 1679
e 2538   **f** 5103   **g** 9245
h 6410

Practice

1 Approximations will vary

a $4172 \times 5 \approx 4200 \times 5 = 21\,000$

		4	1	7	2
$\times$					5
(4000×5)	2	0	0	0	0
(100×5)			5	0	0
(70×5)				3	5	0
(2×5)					1	0
	2	0	8	6	0

b $3652 \times 3 = 10\,956$

c $2936 \times 4 = 11\,744$

d $3845 \times 5 = 19\,225$

e $2463 \times 4 = 9852$

f $5637 \times 6 = 33\,822$

g $5418 \times 7 = 37\,926$

h $6247 \times 6 = 37\,482$

i $7246 \times 8 = 57\,968$

j $6843 \times 7 = 47\,901$

k $7476 \times 9 = 67\,284$

l $6947 \times 8 = 55\,576$

Refresher

1 a	b
$7 \times 6 = 42$	$4 \times 9 = 36$
$2 \times 6 = 12$	$1 \times 9 = 9$
$4 \times 6 = 24$	$7 \times 9 = 63$
$3 \times 6 = 18$	$3 \times 9 = 27$
$5 \times 6 = 30$	$6 \times 9 = 54$
$6 \times 6 = 36$	$8 \times 9 = 72$
$8 \times 6 = 48$	$9 \times 9 = 81$

c	d
$2 \times 7 = 14$	$3 \times 8 = 24$
$7 \times 7 = 49$	$10 \times 8 = 80$
$0 \times 7 = 0$	$7 \times 8 = 56$
$3 \times 7 = 21$	$1 \times 8 = 8$
$4 \times 7 = 28$	$2 \times 8 = 16$
$8 \times 7 = 56$	$8 \times 8 = 64$
$6 \times 7 = 42$	$9 \times 8 = 72$

Challenge

1

567	2835	14 175	70 875	354 375
189	945	4725	23 625	118 125
63	315	1575	7875	39 375
21	105	525	2625	13 125
$\times 3 \uparrow$ 7	35	175	875	4375

$\times 5 \rightarrow$

Practice

1 a $1873 \times 4 = 7492$

b $2736 \times 5 = 13\,680$

c $2432 \times 5 = 9728$

d $3347 \times 3 = 10\,041$

e $4759 \times 5 = 23\,795$

f $2653 \times 6 = 15\,918$

g $3748 \times 9 = 33\,732$

h $4592 \times 8 = 36\,736$

i $2963 \times 7 = 20\,741$

j $3264 \times 6 = 19\,584$

k $5643 \times 7 = 39\,501$

l $4976 \times 8 = 39\,808$

m $6475 \times 6 = 38\,850$

n $5847 \times 4 = 23\,388$

o $4346 \times 8 = 34\,768$

2 Approximations will vary

a $4867 \times 5 = 24\,335$ stamps sold

b $3956 \times 6 = 23\,736$ letters collected per day

c $7002 \times 6 = 42\,012$ letters delivered per week

d $(3265 \times 3) + (5632 \times 3) = 26\,691$ stamps sold

e $2437 \times 5 = 12\,185$ trips

f $2658 \times 6 = 15\,948$ letters

Refresher

Approximations will vary

Challenge

1 $4998 \times 2 = 9996$
$1666 \times 6 = 9996$
$3332 \times 3 = 9996$
$2499 \times 4 = 9996$
$1428 \times 7 = 9996$

2 $5020 \times 3 = 15060$
$3012 \times 5 = 15060$
$2510 \times 6 = 15060$
$3765 \times 4 = 15060$
$7530 \times 2 = 15060$

Week 3, Lesson 4 – Pages 26 and 27

Practice

1 a $6.0 + 0.3$ **b** $7.0 + 0.2$
   c $3.0 + 0.5$ **d** $4.0 + 0.8$
   e $8.0 + 0.9$

2 a $20.0 + 4.0 + 0.6$
   b $10.0 + 8.0 + 0.3$
   c $6.0 + 0.4 + 0.02$
   d $7.0 + 0.7 + 0.08$
   e $3.0 + 0.5 + 0.09$

3 a $4.0 + 0.8 + 0.02$
   b $9.0 + 0.3$
   c $10.0 + 5.0 + 0.4$
   d $7.0 + 0.03$
   e $2.0 + 0.9$

4 a $10.0 + 2.0 + 0.6$
   b $9.0 + 0.9 + 0.02$
   c $4.0 + 0.3 + 0.05$
   d $20.0 + 6.0 + 0.1$
   e $8.0 + 0.09$

5 Answers will vary

Refresher

1 a $4 \leftarrow 4.6 \rightarrow$ (5)
   b (3) $\leftarrow 3.4 \rightarrow 4$
   c $7 \leftarrow 7.8 \rightarrow$ (8)
   d $25 \leftarrow 25.9 \rightarrow$ (26)
   e (12) $\leftarrow 12.1 \rightarrow 13$

2 a $3 \leftarrow 3.67 \rightarrow$ (4)
   b $4 \leftarrow 4.82 \rightarrow$ (5)

   c (8) $\leftarrow 8.46 \rightarrow 9$
   d (9) $\leftarrow 9.35 \rightarrow 10$
   e (5) $\leftarrow 5.02 \rightarrow 6$

3 a (16) $\leftarrow 16.1 \rightarrow 17$
   b (7) $\leftarrow 7.06 \rightarrow 8$
   c $14 \leftarrow 14.92 \rightarrow$ (15)
   d $31 \leftarrow 31.7 \rightarrow$ (32)
   e (48) $\leftarrow 48.3 \rightarrow 49$

Challenge

1 a $8 \times 4 = 32$ **b** $7 \times 6 = 42$
     $8 \times 7 = 56$ $7 \times 5 = 35$
     $5 \times 7 = 35$ $6 \times 7 = 42$
     $5 \times 8 = 40$ $7 \times 7 = 49$
   c $13 \times 6 = 78$ **d** $8 \times 3 = 24$
     $13 \times 3 = 39$ $5 \times 8 = 40$
     $16 \times 2 = 32$ $6 \times 4 = 24$
     $12 \times 6 = 72$ $8 \times 5 = 40$
   e $5 \times 3 = 15$
     $5 \times 3 = 15$
     $5 \times 4 = 20$
     $3 \times 6 = 18$

2 a $58.8 - 31.2 = 27.6$
   b $45.5 - 33.5 = 12$
   c $79.2 - 32.6 = 46.6$
   d $43.44 - 23.32 = 20.12$
   e $21.28 - 13.86 = 7.42$

Week 3 Lesson 5 – Pages 28 and 29

Practice

1 a £17 325
   b £11.84
   c £23256 total value £11 628 profit
   d £1612
   e £44.88 total cost £5.12 change
   f £42

Refresher

1 a $8 \times £24 = £192$
   b $16 \times £25 = £400$
   c $36 \times £6 = £216$
   d Yes $(25 \times £7.48 = £187)$

e $(18 \times £24) - (12 \times £25) = £132$

f You can buy 6 sets of headphones
$(6 \times £15 = £90)$

g $£67 + £15 + £18 = £100$

h $(2 \times £2475) + (4 \times £25) = £5050$

i No, you do not have enough money
$(6 \times £3.50 = £21)$

Challenge
1 Answers will vary
2 Answers will vary
3 Answers will vary

Week 4, Lesson 1 – Pages 30 and 31

Practice
1 a $1\frac{3}{4}$ **b** $1\frac{4}{5}$ **c** $1\frac{5}{7}$ **d** $\frac{8}{6}$ **e** $\frac{10}{7}$ **f** $\frac{14}{9}$

2 a $1\frac{7}{8}$ **b** $1\frac{1}{3}$ **c** $1\frac{1}{8}$ **d** $2\frac{1}{6}$ **e** $4\frac{1}{4}$

f $5\frac{1}{2}$ **g** $3\frac{1}{5}$ **h** $2\frac{4}{9}$ **i** $1\frac{1}{10}$ **j** $1\frac{1}{100}$

3 a $\frac{9}{6}$ **b** $\frac{9}{5}$ **c** $\frac{9}{7}$ **d** $\frac{20}{8}$ **e** $\frac{7}{3}$

f $\frac{26}{10}$ **g** $\frac{26}{9}$ **h** $\frac{31}{12}$ **i** $\frac{33}{10}$ **j** $\frac{318}{100}$

Refresher
1 a $1\frac{1}{3}$ **b** $1\frac{2}{6}$ **c** $1\frac{3}{4}$ **d** $1\frac{1}{2}$ **e** $1\frac{1}{7}$ **f** $1\frac{2}{8}$

2 a $\frac{8}{6}$ **b** $\frac{8}{5}$ **c** $\frac{7}{7}$ **d** $\frac{19}{10}$ **e** $\frac{7}{4}$ **f** $\frac{14}{9}$

Challenge
1 a $1\frac{1}{8}$, $1\frac{21}{100}$, $1\frac{1}{3}$, $1\frac{8}{10}$, $1\frac{7}{8}$, $2\frac{1}{6}$, $2\frac{4}{9}$, $3\frac{1}{5}$, $4\frac{1}{4}$, $5\frac{1}{2}$

b $\frac{9}{7}$, $\frac{9}{6}$, $\frac{9}{5}$, $\frac{7}{3}$, $\frac{20}{8}$, $\frac{31}{12}$, $\frac{26}{10}$, $\frac{26}{9}$, $\frac{318}{100}$, $\frac{33}{10}$

Week 4, Lesson 2 – Pages 32 and 33

Practice
1 a $\frac{1}{2}$ is 3 times $\frac{1}{6}$ **b** $\frac{1}{2}$ is 4 times $\frac{1}{8}$

c $\frac{1}{2}$ is 5 times $\frac{1}{10}$ **d** $\frac{1}{2}$ is 6 times $\frac{1}{12}$

e $\frac{1}{2}$ is 7 times $\frac{1}{14}$

2 a $\frac{1}{4}$ is 4 times $\frac{1}{16}$ **b** $\frac{1}{4}$ is 3 times $\frac{1}{12}$

c $\frac{1}{4}$ is 5 times $\frac{1}{20}$ **d** $\frac{1}{10}$ is 10 times $\frac{1}{100}$

e $\frac{1}{10}$ is 3 times $\frac{1}{30}$ **f** $\frac{1}{10}$ is 4 times $\frac{1}{40}$

g $\frac{1}{5}$ is 3 times $\frac{1}{15}$ **h** $\frac{1}{5}$ is 20 times $\frac{1}{100}$

Refresher
1 a $\frac{1}{2}$ is twice $\frac{1}{4}$ **b** $\frac{1}{4}$ is twice $\frac{1}{8}$

c $\frac{1}{3}$ is twice $\frac{1}{6}$ **d** $\frac{1}{5}$ is twice $\frac{1}{10}$

e $\frac{1}{6}$ is twice $\frac{1}{12}$ **f** $\frac{1}{10}$ is twice $\frac{1}{20}$

g $\frac{1}{7}$ is twice $\frac{1}{14}$ **h** $\frac{1}{8}$ is twice $\frac{1}{16}$

Challenge
Open

Week 4, Lesson 3 – Pages 34 and 35

Practice
1 a $\frac{1}{3}$ **b** $\frac{1}{3}$ **c** $\frac{1}{3}$ **d** $\frac{1}{3}$

e $\frac{1}{2}$ **f** $\frac{1}{3}$ **g** $\frac{3}{8}$ **h** $\frac{2}{3}$

i $\frac{3}{5}$ **j** $\frac{1}{4}$ **k** $\frac{3}{10}$ **l** $\frac{9}{20}$

m $\frac{3}{4}$ **n** $\frac{7}{18}$ **o** $\frac{4}{5}$ **p** $\frac{3}{7}$

2 a $\frac{6}{10}$ **b** $\frac{8}{14}$ **c** $\frac{10}{18}$ **d** $\frac{6}{14}$

e $\frac{2}{8}$ **f** $\frac{6}{20}$ **g** $\frac{4}{12}$ **h** $\frac{10}{16}$

i $\frac{8}{10}$ **j** $\frac{4}{18}$ **k** $\frac{6}{16}$ **l** $\frac{4}{16}$

m $\frac{10}{12}$ **n** $\frac{8}{10}$ **o** $\frac{10}{14}$ **p** $\frac{6}{18}$

Refresher
1 a $\frac{1}{2}$ **b** $\frac{2}{4}$ **c** $\frac{2}{6}$ **d** $\frac{1}{3}$ **e** $\frac{1}{4}$

f $\frac{2}{8}$ **g** $\frac{3}{4}$ **h** $\frac{3}{6}$ **i** $\frac{3}{9}$ **j** $\frac{4}{6}$

2 a $\frac{1}{2}$ **b** $\frac{2}{4}$ **c** $\frac{1}{3}$ **d** $\frac{2}{3}$ **e** $\frac{1}{4}$

f $\frac{2}{6}$ **g** $\frac{3}{4}$ **h** $\frac{4}{6}$ **i** $\frac{3}{5}$ **j** $\frac{2}{5}$

Challenge
Answers will vary

Week 4, Lesson 4 – Pages 36 and 37

Practice
1 a 0.8 or 8 tenths

b 0.3 or 3 tenths

c 0.02 or 2 hundredths

d 0.004 or 4 thousandths

e 0.06 or 6 hundredths

f 0.007 or 7 thousandths

2 a 4.005, 4.106, 4.293, 4.687, 4.972

b 1.073, 2.637, 3.612, 4.637, 5.892

c 0.045, 0.832, 1.405, 1.504, 2.832

Collins Primary Maths

d 0.462, 0.513, 4.624, 5.130, 5.310
e 6.526, 6.581, 6.723, 6.729, 6.735

3

a |4·67|4·671|4·672|4·673|4·674|4·675|4·676|4·677|4·678|4·679|4·68|

b |2·89|2·891|2·892|2·893|2·894|2·895|2·896|2·897|2·898|2·899|2·90|

c |3·31|3·311|3·312|3·313|3·314|3·315|3·316|3·317|3·318|3·319|3·32|

d |5·04|5·041|5·042|5·043|5·044|5·045|5·046|5·047|5·048|5·049|5·05|

e |6·53|6·531|6·532|6·533|6·534|6·535|6·536|6·537|6·538|6·539|6·54|

f |7·22|7·221|7·222|7·223|7·224|7·225|7·226|7·227|7·228|7·229|7·23|

Refresher

1 a 0.06 or 6 hundredths
 b 0.5 or 5 tenths
 c 0.09 or 9 hundredths
 d 0.07 or 7 hundredths
 e 0.8 or 8 tenths
2 a 1.63, 2.04, 3.72, 4.89, 5.62
 b 4.12, 4.51, 4.66, 4.86, 4.93
 c 0.72, 0.74, 0.75, 0.78, 0.79
 d 1.51, 1.55, 1.59, 1.82, 1.87
 e 2.14, 2.22, 2.41, 4.12, 4.21

3 a |4·2|4·21|4·22|4·23|4·24|4·25|4·26|4·27|4·28|4·29|4·3|

 b |2·7|2·71|2·72|2·73|2·74|2·75|2·76|2·77|2·78|2·79|2·8|

 c |5·5|5·51|5·52|5·53|5·54|5·55|5·56|5·57|5·58|5·59|5·6|

 d |3·3|3·31|3·32|3·33|3·34|3·35|3·36|3·37|3·38|3·39|3·4|

 e |7·1|7·11|7·12|7·13|7·14|7·15|7·16|7·17|7·18|7·19|7·2|

Challenge

1 24
2 No more different arrangements of the digits can be found.
3 2.568, 2.586, 2.658, 2.685, 2.856, 2.865, 5.268, 5.286, 5.628, 5.682, 5.826, 5.862, 6.258, 6.285, 6.528, 6.582, 6.825, 6.852, 8.256, 8.265, 8.526, 8.562, 8.625, 8.652

Week 4, Lesson 5 – Pages 38 and 39

Practice

1 a 0.14 and $\frac{14}{100}$ or 0.41 and $\frac{41}{100}$
 b 0.86 and $\frac{86}{100}$ or 0.68 and $\frac{68}{100}$

c 0.23 and $\frac{23}{100}$ or 0.32 and $\frac{32}{100}$
d 0.5 and $\frac{1}{2}$ or 0.2 and $\frac{1}{5}$
e 0.6 and $\frac{3}{5}$ or 0.5 and $\frac{3}{6}$
f 0.78 and $\frac{78}{100}$ or 0.87 and $\frac{87}{100}$
g 0.2 or $\frac{2}{10}$
h 0.528 and $\frac{528}{1000}$
i 0.3 and $\frac{30}{100}$ **j** 0.25 and $\frac{1}{4}$

Refresher

1 a 0.5 and $\frac{1}{2}$ or 0.2 and $\frac{1}{5}$
 b 0.5 and $\frac{4}{8}$ or 0.8 and $\frac{4}{5}$
 c 0.4 and $\frac{4}{10}$ **d** 0.25 and $\frac{1}{4}$
 e $\frac{21}{100}$ and 0.21 or 0.12 and $\frac{12}{100}$
 f 0.7 and $\frac{7}{10}$ **g** 0.6 and $\frac{3}{5}$
 h 0.83 and $\frac{83}{100}$ or 0.38 and $\frac{38}{100}$
 i 0.6 and $\frac{6}{10}$

Challenge

1 a 1.93 **b** 0.047 **c** 0.002
 d 0.673 **e** 0.405

Week 5, Lesson 1 – Pages 40 and 41

Practice

1 a 1 gram is 0.001 kg
 b 1 centimetre is 0.01 m
 c 1 millilitre is 0.001 l
 d 1 metre is 0.001 km
 e 1 millimetre is 0.1 cm
2 a 450 cm or 4.5 m
 b 6980 m or 6.98 km
 c 2846 m or 2.846 km
 d 41 mm or 4.1 cm
 e 216 cm or 2.16 m
 f 3248 m or 3.248 km
 g 68 mm or 6.8 cm
 h 1520 m or 1.52 km
 i 3872 m or 3.872 km
 j 422 cm or 4.22 m
3 a 1987 ml or 1.987 l
 b 1537 ml or 1.537 l
 c 1395 ml or 1.395 l

d 2775 ml or 2.775 l

e 2250 ml or 2.25 l

f 3830 ml or 3.83 l

g 4414 ml or 4.414 l

h 4912 ml or 4.912 l

4 a 2535 g or 2.535 kg

b 3385 g or 3.385 kg

c 4585 g or 4.585 kg

d 5846 g or 5.846 kg

e 4229 g or 4.229 kg

f 6554 g or 6.554 kg

g 7313 g or 7.313 kg

h 8800 g or 8.8 kg

Refresher

1 a 11 500 ml   b 11 750 ml

c 11 900 ml   d 11 540 ml

e 11 665 ml   f 11 915 ml

g 11 648 ml   h 11 947 ml

i 11 824 ml   j 11 953 ml

2 a 11 600 ml   b 11 350 ml

c 11 440 ml   d 11 548 ml

e 11 390 ml   f 11 472 ml

g 11 461 ml   h 11 228 ml

i 11 16 ml   j 11 95 ml

Challenge

1 a 0.75 kg   b 4.5 cm

c 0.567 km   d 0.854 kg

e 0.203 km   f 1.254 kg

g 1.763 km   h 1.965 l

i 2.763 kg   j 2.653 km

Week 5, Lesson 2 – Pages 42 and 43

Practice

1 a $\frac{8}{10}$ cotton, $\frac{1}{10}$ polyamide, $\frac{1}{10}$ Lycra

b $\frac{3}{4}$ wool, $\frac{1}{4}$ acrylic

c $\frac{1}{8}$ elastane, $\frac{7}{8}$ acrylic

d 62.5% or $\frac{5}{8}$

2 a 52%, $\frac{5}{8}$, 67%   b 42%, $\frac{2}{6}$, $\frac{4}{12}$, 27%

c 11%, $\frac{11}{100}$, $\frac{3}{20}$ d 35%, $\frac{4}{9}$, $\frac{4}{8}$

e $\frac{3}{16}$, 13%, $\frac{1}{4}$

3 Answers will vary

4 Answers will vary

Refresher

1 a $\frac{1}{2}$ b $\frac{1}{4}$ c $\frac{3}{4}$ d $\frac{1}{10}$ e $\frac{1}{5}$

2   trousers – 50% polyamide

shirt – 25% Lycra

jumper – 80% wool

T-shirt – 50% cotton

Challenge

1 a $\frac{1}{8}$, 13%, $\frac{2}{8}$, 27%, $\frac{3}{8}$, 40%

b 1%, 22%, $\frac{1}{3}$, 35%, $\frac{2}{3}$, 71%

c $\frac{3}{8}$, 45%, $\frac{1}{2}$, 68%, $\frac{3}{4}$, 86%

d 9%, $\frac{1}{10}$, 49%, $\frac{5}{10}$, 74%, $\frac{8}{10}$

e 48%, $\frac{3}{6}$, 51%, $\frac{5}{8}$, 66%, $\frac{2}{3}$

Week 5, Lesson 3 – Pages 44 and 45

Practice

1 a 6

b 3 or $\frac{1}{8}$

c 66 $\frac{2}{3}$% or 66.666%, $\frac{2}{3}$

d 2 or 3

e about 20%

2 a 240

b 224

c 20%

d about 33% or about 106 children

e about 25%

Refresher

1 a 10   b 5

c 15 or 75%   d 2

e 6, 70% or 14 children

Challenge

Open

Week 5, Lesson 4 – Pages 46 and 47

Practice

1 a Ratio: 5 white units to every 1 red
Proportion: 5 in every 6 units
are white

 Collins Primary Maths

b Ratio: 4 white units to every 2 red
   Proportion: 4 in every 6 units
   are white

c Ratio: 5 white units to every 3 red
   Proportion: 5 in every 8 units
   are white

d Ratio: 3 white units to every 2 red
   Proportion: 3 in every 5 units
   are white

e Ratio: 6 white units to every 1 red
   Proportion: 6 in every 7 units
   are white

f Ratio: 5 white units to every 2 red
   Proportion: 5 in every 7 units
   are white

Refresher

1 a The ratio is 1 red square to every 2
      blue squares.

b The ratio is 2 red squares to every
   3 blue squares.

c The ratio is 1 red square to every 3
   blue square.

d The ratio is 1 red square to every 3
   blue squares.

e The ratio is 2 red squares to every
   4 blue squares.

Challenge

1 a 20 white, 4 red   **b** 20 white, 10 red
   c 25 white, 15 red **d** 21 white, 14 red
   e 36 white, 6 red   **f** 35 white, 14 red

2 Using the proportion of white units in
   each pattern found in Practice

Week 5, Lesson 5 – Pages 48 and 49

Practice

1 a 1:2
   b 1 in 3 or $\frac{1}{3}$
   c 20 girls and 10 boys

2 a 1:5   **b** 5 eggs

3 a 5
b 1 in every 11 or $\frac{1}{11}$

4 a 2:4 or 1:2
   b 2 in every 6 or $\frac{2}{6}$ or $\frac{1}{3}$

c 6   **d** 12

5 a 12   **b** 20
   c 3 in every 8 or $\frac{3}{8}$
   d 5 in every 8 or $\frac{5}{8}$

Refresher

1 a 2:1   **b** 8   **c** 4
2 a 1:3   **b** 4   **c** 18
3 a 2:3   **b** 8   **c** 12

Challenge

Open

Week 6, Lesson 1 – Pages 50 and 51

Practice

1 a $\frac{1}{6}$ **b** 0   **c** $\frac{1}{2}$ **d** $\frac{2}{6}$ or $\frac{1}{3}$
   e $\frac{1}{2}$ **f** $\frac{4}{6}$ or $\frac{2}{3}$ **g** 1

2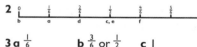

3 a $\frac{1}{6}$ **b** $\frac{3}{6}$ or $\frac{1}{2}$ **c** 1
   d 0   **e** $\frac{4}{6}$ or $\frac{2}{3}$ **f** blue

4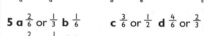

5 a $\frac{2}{6}$ or $\frac{1}{3}$ **b** $\frac{1}{6}$ **c** $\frac{3}{6}$ or $\frac{1}{2}$ **d** $\frac{4}{6}$ or $\frac{2}{3}$
   e $\frac{2}{6}$ or $\frac{1}{3}$ **f** 0   **g** 2 and 4

6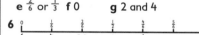

Refresher

1 a Unlikely   **b** Even chance
   c Impossible   **d** Even chance
   e Likely   **f** Certain

2

Challenge

1 a 0.1   **b** 0   **c** 0.5
   d 0.2   **e** 0.3   **f** 0.5
   g 0.4   **h** 0.8   **i** 1

2

Week 6, Lesson 2 – Pages 52 and 53

Practice

1 a $\frac{2}{6}$ or $\frac{1}{3}$ b 10
  c Answers will vary
  d Answers will vary
2 a Red   b $\frac{3}{4}$ c 30
3 Answers will vary

Refresher

1 a $\frac{1}{6}$ b 5
  c Answers will vary
  d Answers will vary
2 a 10
  b Answers will vary
  c Answers will vary
  d Answers will vary

Challenge

1 a $\frac{3}{10}$ or 0.3   b 9
  c Answers will vary
  d Answers will vary
2 a 18
  b Answers will vary
  c Answers will vary
  d Answers will vary

Week 6, Lesson 3 – Pages 54 and 55

Practice

1

Length (seconds)	Tally	Total
1–10	JHT I	6
11–20	JHT JHT JHT II	17
21–30	JHT III	8
31–40	III	3
41–50	I	1

2

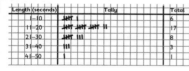

3 a 8   b 4
  c 11–20 seconds   d 23

Refresher

1 a 6   b 1–10 minutes
  c 41–50 minutes   d 3

2

Challenge

1

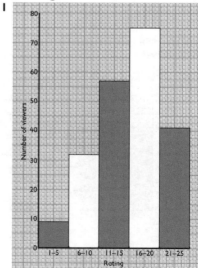

2 16–20
3 116
4 43
5 164
6 214

 Collins Primary Maths

Week 6, Lesson 4 – Pages 56 and 57

Practice

1 a 32   b 30   c 6–10 d 49   e 16

2

Score	Number of games
1–5	17
6–10	32
11–15	12
16–20	9
21–25	5
26–30	2

3

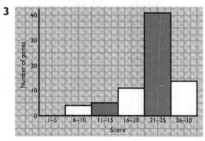

4 a 21–25   b 6
  c 9   d 52
  e Yes. The tallest bar is 21–25.

Refresher

1

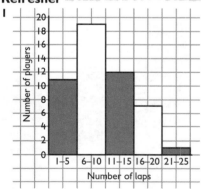

2 a 12   b 11
  c 6–10   d 19
  e Only one player achieved 21–25 laps without crashing

Challenge

1 a 21 seconds
  b 4
  c 10
  d 39 players had lap times between 41 and 50 seconds
  e 15

Week 6, Lesson 5 – Pages 58 and 59

Practice

1 Answers will vary
2 Answers will vary
3 Answers will vary
4 Answers will vary
5 Answers will vary
6 a 11
  b 66
  c 55
  d Answers will vary
  e Answers will vary
  f Answers will vary

Refresher

1 a 7   b 2   c 6   d 9, 10
  e 5   f 100   g 2, 7 h 7
2 a 4   b 5   c 3   d 8
  e 4   f 700   g 8   h 7
3 Answers will vary
4 Answers will vary

Challenge

1 a For example: 2, 6, 6 and 6, 6, 8
  b 60, 60, 63
  c 6, 6, 9
  d For example: 6, 9, 20, 20 and 2, 6, 20, 20
  e 11, 11, 19, 21
  f For example: 20, 20, 20, 30 and 20, 20, 21, 30
  g For example: 60, 63, 99, 99, 100 and 20, 99, 99, 99, 99
  h For example: 6, 6, 6, 6, 7 and 8, 8, 8, 9, 9
  i For example: 11, 11, 19, 19, 21 and 11, 11, 19, 19, 30

Week 7, Lesson 1 - Pages 60 and 61

Practice

1 a 3, 4, 5, 6, 9 median = 5
  b 2, 2, 2, 2, 8, 8, 8 median = 2
  c 4, 4, 4, 4, 4, 9, 9, 9, 9 median = 4
  d 10, 20, 30, 30, 50 median = 30
  e 18, 20, 28, 34, 38, 42, 69 median = 34
  f 1, 1, 2, 2, 3, 3, 4, 4, 6, 7, 9 median = 3
  g 35, 40, 45, 45, 50, 70, 75, 80, 80
    median = 50
  h 1, 1, 1, 1, 1, 3, 3, 3, 3, 3, 9, 9, 9
    median = 3

2 a 4   **b** 4   **c** 9   **d** 4
  e 40 **f** 350 **g** 5 **h** 5.5

3 a 583 **b** 1650 **c** 835 **d** 2685
  e 4900 **f** 3927 **g** 10612

4 a 64g **b** £9 **c** 180cm **d** £1
  e 6.5g **f** 1100ml **g** £6.02

Refresher

1 a 5   **b** 2   **c** 6   **d** 6
  e 80 **f** 28 **g** 59 **h** 40

2 a 8   **b** 3.5 **c** 2   **d** 25
  e 3.5 **f** 53 **g** 425 **h** 19.5

3 a 9   **b** 3   **c** 4
  d 52.5 **e** 9   **f** 8.5

Challenge

1 Crunchy Crisps 30, Crispy Crisps 35 (highest mode), Golden Fries 27
2 Crunchy Crisps 36 (highest median), Crispy Crisps 35, Golden Fries 28.5
3 Crunchy Crisps 9, Crispy Crisps 3 (narrowest range), Golden Fries 26
4 Crispy Crisps, because it has a more consistent number of crisps (lowest range), and its median is only one less than Crunchy Crisps.

Week 7, Lesson 2 - Pages 62 and 63

Practice

1 a 9   **b** 10 **c** 5   **d** 2.4
  e 14 **f** 2   **g** 3   **h** 9

2 a 250g   **b** 4g   **c** 200g

d 40g   **e** 9g   **f** 23g

3 a 83.5 **b** 54.5 **c** 282 **d** 32
  e 2712.5 **f** 68.25 **g** 59.4

4 a £5.50 **b** £9.25 **c** £65.50 **d** £2.42
  e £5.50 **f** £4.10 **g** £1.48

Refresher

1 a 13   **b** 21   **c** 75
  d 300   **e** 48   **f** 205

2 a 9   **b** 6   **c** 4
  d 7   **e** 50   **f** 6

3 a 6   **b** 4   **c** 20
  d 100   **e** 9   **f** 8

4 a 3   **b** 20   **c** 12
  d 50   **e** 3   **f** 200

Challenge

	Median	Mean	Range
1	63	59	66
2	290g	281.5g	533g
3	£7.18	£7.65	£15.16
4	31.2cm	33.6cm	32.6cm
5	2375	3395	8750
6	216kg	303kg	495kg
7	319ml	422.5ml	774ml
8	31s	45.8s	81s
9	100p	£1.56	£4.82
10	207cm	202.5cm	209cm

Week 7, Lesson 3 - Pages 64 and 65

Practice

1	Cost of Crystal Hi-fi (£)	Cost of JVC Hi-fi (£)	N° hi-fi's in stock
a mode	210	499, 500	5
b range	50	133	23
c mean	230	467	7
d median	225	499	5

2 a JVC
  b Crystal
  c JVC. There is a bigger difference in price among the different shops.

Collins Primary Maths

4

	Cost of Crystal Hi-fi (£)	Cost of JVC Hi-fi (£)	N° hi-fi's in stock
a median	222.5	499	5
b mode	210	499	5
range	50	133	23

c It has been reduced by £2.50
d There is now only one mode
f Crystal £227.50, JVC £471

Refresher

1 a 2   b £38, £42   c 200g, 350g
2 a 4   b £210   c 49g
3 a 7   b 6   c £55   d 43g
4 a 55   b £9   c 683g

Challenge

1

Name of biscuit	Number of biscuits	Price	Weight
Ginger Snaps	10	85p	200g
Coconut Swirls	12	70p	160g
Chocolate Fingers	10	£1.20	90g
Cream Sandwich	20	£1.12	500g
Strawberry Hearts	15	96p	300g
Lemon Drops	10	75p	200g
Butter Wheels	8	£1.00	90g
Fruit Bars	12	£1.42	180g
Cherry Spots	20	£2.35	700g

2

	N° biscuits	Price	Weight
mode	10	No mode	90g 200g
median	12	£1.00	200g
mean	13	£1.15	268.9g
range	12	£1.65	610g

Week 8, Lesson 1 – Pages 66 and 67

Practice

1

Shape	Total number of faces	Horizontal faces	Vertical faces
cube	6	2	4
triangular prism	5	2	3
square-based pyramid	5	1	0
cone	2	1	0

2

Shape	Total number of edges	Horizontal edges	Vertical edges
cube	12	8	4
triangular prism	9	6	3
square-based pyramid	8	4	0
cone	1	1	0

3 a AB//DC, AD//BC and PQ//SR, PS//QR
  b AD⊥DC, DC⊥CB, BA⊥AD, AB⊥BC
    and PS⊥SR, SR⊥RQ, QP⊥PS, PQ⊥QR
  c 4 and 6

Refresher

1 a The horizontal edges are AD and BC.
  b The vertical edges are AB and DC.
  c Edge AD is parallel to BC.
  d Edge DC is parallel to AB.
2   AD⊥DC, DC⊥CB, CB⊥BA, BA⊥AD

Challenge

1 a

	Horizontal faces	Perpendicular faces
A	2	5
B	1	2
C	1	0
D	1	0

b Position A is the only one in which the pentagonal prism can have more than one horizontal face and two perpendicular faces. However the pyramid is placed, no face can be perpendicular.

2 a

	Pairs of parallel edges
A	10
B	10
C	2
D	2

b For shapes A and B, each rectangular face has 2 pairs of parallel edges. There are 5 rectangular faces and therefore 10 pairs of parallel edges. Shapes C and D have only one rectangular face and therefore only two pairs of parallel edges.

Week 8, Lesson 2 – Pages 68 and 69

Practice

1, 2 and 3 Open

4

Quadrilateral	Opposite sides equal	Opposite sides parallel	Opposite angles equal	All sides equal	All right angles
rectangle	✓	✓	✓	✗	✓
square	✓	✓	✓	✓	✓
parallelogram	✓	✓	✓	✗	✗
rhombus	✓	✓	✓	✓	✗

Refresher

1 Shape A – region 1
Shape B – region 2
Shape C – region 4
Shape D – region 3
Shape E – region 4
Shape F – region 3
Shape G – region 1
Shape H – region 2
Shape I – region 1
Shape J – region 4
Shape K – region 1
Shape L – region 3

Challenge

Quadrilaterals	Similar properties	Different properties
square and rectangle	both have 4 right angles	square has 4 equal sides rectangle has opposite sides equal
square and rhombus	all sides equal	square has all right angles rhombus has no right angles
rectangle and parallelogram	opposite sides equal and parallel	rectangle has all right angles parallelogram has no right angles rectangle has line symmetry
rhombus and parallelogram	opposite sides parallel	rhombus has all sides equal, parallelogram does not rhombus has line symmetry

Week 8, Lesson 3 – Pages 70 and 71

Practice

1 Shape A – parallelogram
Shape B – kite
Shape C – rectangle
Shape D – kite
Shape E – rectangle
Shape F – trapezium
Shape G – trapezium
Shape H – rhombus
Shape I – kite
Shape J – trapezium
Shape K – square
Shape L – parallelogram

2 a F, G, J   b B, D, I   c B, D, G, I

Refresher

1 Open
2 Open

Challenge

1

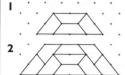

2

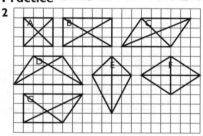

3 The area of the second diagram is $2\frac{1}{4}$ times the area of the first.

Week 8, Lesson 4 – Pages 72 and 73

Practice

2

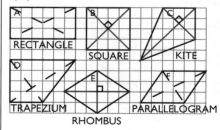

3

Property	Quadrilateral						
	A	B	C	D	E	F	G
4 sides equal	✓	✗	✗	✗	✗	✓	✗
4 angles equal	✓	✓	✗	✗	✗	✗	✗
diagonals are same length	✓	✓	✗	✓	✗	✗	✗
diagonals cut each other in half	✓	✓	✓	✓	✗	✗	✗
diagonals intersect at right angles	✓	✗	✗	✗	✓	✓	✗
a diagonal is an axis of symmetry	✓	✗	✗	✗	✓	✓	✗

Refresher

1, 2, 3 and 4

RECTANGLE
SQUARE
KITE
TRAPEZIUM
RHOMBUS
PARALLELOGRAM

Challenge

1 The statement is true.
2 The intersection is at the mid-point of each diagonal.
3 The diagonals of rectangles and parallelograms are similar in that the diagonals cut each other in half. However, they are different in that the diagonals of rectangles are equal but this is not true of parallelograms.

Week 8, Lesson 5 – Pages 74 and 75

Practice

1 a A (−3, 2), B (3,2), C (3, −4), D (−3, −4)
 b E (−2, 4), F (3, −1), G (1, −3), H (−4, 2)
 c K (−3, 2), L (3, 3), M (2, −1), N (−4, −2)
2 a B   b D   c C   d F   e E
3 a rectangle   b kite
4 (−4, −3)
5 a

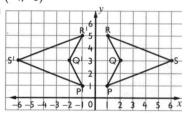

 b (−1, 1), (−2, 3), (−1, 5), (−6, 3)

Refresher

1 A (−5, 5)   B (−2, 4)
 C (−4, 3)   D (1, 3)
 E (−3, 2)   F (3, 2)
 G (−2, 1)   H (5, 1)

2

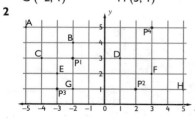

Challenge

a

	1st quadrant	2nd quadrant	3rd quadrant	4th quadrant
A	(1, 1)	(−1, 1)	(−1, −1)	(1, −1)
B	(4, 1)	(−4, 1)	(−4, −1)	(4, −1)
C	(1, 6)	(−1, 6)	(−1, −6)	(1, −6)

b

	1st quadrant	2nd quadrant	3rd quadrant	4th quadrant
A	(1, 1)	(−1, 1)	(−1, −1)	(1, −1)
B	(4, 1)	(−4, 1)	(−4, −1)	(1, −4)
C	(1, 6)	(−6, 1)	(−1, −6)	(6, −1)

Week 9, Lesson 1 – Pages 76 and 77

Practice

1 Grid 2

Shape	x-axis	y-axis
A	−4	5
B	−1	5
C	2	5
D	5	5
E	8	5

translation: 3 to the right

Grid 3

Shape	x-axis	y-axis
A	6	7
B	4	6
C	2	5
D	0	4
E	−2	3

translation: 2 to the left and then 1 down

Grid 4

Shape	x-axis	y-axis
A	−4	2
B	0	3
C	4	4
D	8	5
E	12	6

translation: 4 to the right and then 1 up
2 The difference between the coordinates of the corresponding vertices matches the distance and direction of the translated shapes.
3 Open

a

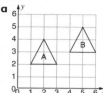

Shape A has been translated 3 to the right, then 1 up.

b

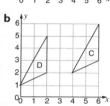

Shape C has been translated 4 to the left, then 1 down.

Challenge

1, 2 and 3

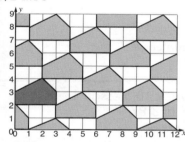

4 Any amount of space can be covered by repeating this shape in the pattern shown. This pattern is called tessellation.

Week 9, Lesson 2 – Pages 78 and 79

Practice

1 a right-angled isosceles triangle
 b right-angled isosceles triangle
 c right-angled isosceles triangle
 d square
 e right-angled isosceles triangle
 f hexagon

2 a Translated – a, e
 b Rotated – b, c, d, f

3 Open

Refresher

1 a equilateral triangle
 b parallelogram
 c hexagon

2

Challenge
Open

Week 9, Lesson 3 – Pages 80 and 81

Practice

1 a P = 2 × (l + b)
     = 2 × (8 + 6) cm
     = 2 × 14 cm
     = 28 cm
 b 24 cm **c** 28 cm **d** 36 cm **e** 38 cm
2 a 30 cm   **b** 48 cm   **c** 74 cm
 d 112 cm   **e** 58 cm
3 a 14 m **b** 14 m **c** 15 m **d** 40 m

Refresher

1 a Perimeter 14 units
 b Perimeter 14 units
 c Perimeter 14 units
 d Perimeter 14 units
 e Perimeter 14 units
 f Perimeter 14 units
 g Perimeter 12 units
 h Perimeter 10 units
 i Perimeter 12 units
 j Perimeter 12 units
 k Perimeter 14 units
 l Perimeter 14 units

Challenge

2 For 1 step P = 4 cm
   For 2 steps P = 8 cm
   For 3 steps P = 12 cm
   For 4 steps P = 16 cm

4

number of steps in staircase	1	2	3	4	5	6
perimeter of staircase	4	8	12	16	20	24

Collins Primary Maths

5 For 10 steps P = 40 cm and for 100 steps P = 400 cm

Week 9, Lesson 4 – Pages 82 and 83
Practice
1 a 10.4 cm   **b** 5.2 cm
   c Mid-point line is $\frac{1}{2}$ the length of the side to which it is parallel.

2 AC measures 14.6 cm and the mid-point is 7.3 cm
   BC measures 7.4 cm and the mid-point is 3.7 cm

3 b Inner rectangle measures 4.8 + 2.4 cm, perimeter is 14.4 cm. Outer rectangle measures 9.6 + 4.8 cm, perimeter is 28.8 cm.
   c Perimeter of the inner rectangle is $\frac{1}{2}$ perimeter of the outer rectangle.
   d Open

4 b Outer rhombus side (5.4 cm) is twice as long as inner rhombus side (2.7 cm).
   d Open

Refresher
1 A 2.8 cm and 5.6 cm
   B 4 cm and 8 cm
   C 5.0 cm and 10.0 cm
   D 2.6 cm and 5.2 cm

2 Open

Challenge
1 Open
2 The perimeter of the largest parallelogram is double the perimeter of the smallest.
3 The sum of the opposite parallel sides of the rectangle is $\frac{1}{2}$ the sum of the parallel sides of the trapezium.

Week 9, Lesson 5 – Pages 84 and 85
Practice
1

Square: 4 pins   Parallelogram: 4 pins   Parallelogram: 4 pins   Hexagon: 6 pins

Rectangle: 6 pins   Square: 4 pins   Square: 8 pins

2

Kite: 6 pins   Kite: 6 pins   Heptagon: 7 pins   Hexagon: 6 pins

3

Refresher
1

Trapezium   Trapezium   Kite

2 Open
Challenge
Open

Week 10, Lesson 1 – Pages 86 and 87
Practice
1 a 6 a.m. – Houston   **b** 21:00 – Tokyo
   c 04:00 – Vancouver   **d** 10 p.m. – Sydney

2 a New York and Athens – 7 hours
   b Rio de Janeiro and Perth – 11 hours
   c Vancouver and Oslo – 9 hours
   d Denver and Johannesburg – 9 hours

3 a London −2 hours: 6:30 p.m.
   b Houston −8 hours: 12:30 p.m.
   c Calcutta +4 hours: 12:30 a.m.
   d Tokyo +7 hours: 3:30 a.m

4 a Calcutta – 00:15 Saturday
   b London – 18:15 Friday
   c New York – 13:15 Friday
   d Perth – 02:15 Saturday

5 Wednesday

Refresher
1 a Athens – 14:00, 2 p.m.
   b Denver – 05:00, 5 a.m.
   c Calcutta – 18:00, 6 p.m.

d Perth – 20:00, 8 p.m.
e Houston – 06:00, 6 a.m.
f Rio de Janeiro – 09:00, 9 a.m.
g Tokyo – 21:00, 9 p.m.
h Oslo – 13:00, 1 p.m.
2 a Athens, Johannesburg
b New York
c Tokyo   **d** Vancouver
e Denver   **f** Sydney

Challenge

1

	American times
Miami	04:00 – 12:00
Houston	03:00 – 11:00
Denver	02:00 – 10:00
Seattle	01:00 – 09:00

2

	London times
Miami	12:30 – 17:00
Houston	13:30 – 17:00
Denver	14:30 – 17:00
Seattle	15:30 – 17:00

Week 10, Lesson 2 – Pages 88 and 89

Practice

1 a 35 cm   **b** 5 cm   **c** 40 cm
2 a 34 cm   **b** 9 cm   **c** 43 cm
3 a 35 cm   **b** 36 cm   **c** 32 cm
4 a

Year	1896	1928	1972	1992
Winning distance	6.35 m	7.73 m	8.24 m	8.67 m

Difference		1.38 m	0.51 m	0.43 m

b 2.32 m
5 a High jump – 0.36 m, long jump – 1.46 m
b High jump – 0.32 m, long jump – 0.92 m

Refresher

1 A Length of see-saw = 50 mm
   Midpoint = 50 mm ÷ 2
          = 25 mm
          = 2.5 cm
   B 72 mm ÷ 2 = 36 mm/3.6 cm
   C 38 mm ÷ 2 = 19 mm/1.9 cm
   D 90 mm ÷ 2 = 45 mm/4.5 cm
   E 66 mm ÷ 2 = 33 mm/3.3 cm
   F 30 mm ÷ 2 = 15 mm/1.5 cm
   G 130 mm ÷ 2 = 65 mm/6.5 cm
   H 150 mm ÷ 2 = 75 mm/7.5 cm

Challenge

1 The bean jumps first to 6.75, then back to 5.375
2 Open
3 Open

Week 10, Lesson 3 – Page 90 and 91

Practice

1 A = 0.65 m   B = 0.88 m
      C = 1.05 m   D = 1.20 m
      E = 1.27 m   F = 1.43 m
2 a 55 cm   **b** 39 cm   **c** 38 cm
3 a 1.92 m **b** 2.31 m **c** 1.93 m **d** 2.63 m
4 150 mm
5 375 m

Refresher

1 Tony – 3.725 km
   Tom – 4.42 km
   Kim – 5.01 km
   Kate – 3.205 km
2 Kenny – 725 m
   Chris – 408 m
   Terry – 570 m
   Ted – 600 m
3 a 1.6 cm **b** 4.2 cm **c** 160 cm **d** 420 cm

Challenge

b Next term is the sum of the 2 previous terms (Fibonacci sequence)
c

	T1	T2	T3	T4	T5	T6	T7	T8	T9	T10
L'gth of path	0.5	1.0	1.5	2.0	2.5	3.0	3.5	4.0	4.5	5.0
N° ways	1	2	3	5	8	13	21	34	55	89

There are 89 ways to arrange the paving stones.

Collins Primary Maths

Week 10, Lesson 4 – Pages 92 and 93

Practice

1

Miles	0	5	10	15	20	25
Kilometres	0	8	16	24	32	40
Co-ordinates	(0, 0)	(5, 8)	(10, 16)	(15, 24)	(20, 32)	(25, 40)

2

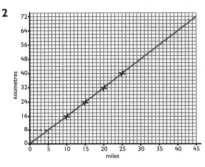

3 a 30 miles = 48 km
  b 40 miles = 64 km
  c 45 miles = 72 km
  d 64 km = 40 miles
  e 56 km = 35 miles
  f 72 km = 45 miles
4 a 12 km = 7.5 miles
  b 16 km = 10 miles
  c 20 km = 12.5 miles
  d 28 km = 17.5 miles
  e 30 km = 19 miles
5 a 100 miles = 160 km
  b 250 miles = 400 km
  c 450 miles = 720 km
  d 505 miles = 808 km
  e 240 km = 150 miles
  f 640 km = 400 miles
  g 480 km = 300 miles
  h 1000 km = 625 miles

Refresher

1

Miles	0	5	10	15
Kilometres	0	8	16	24
Co-ordinates	(0, 0)	(5, 8)	(10, 16)	(15, 24)

3 a 4 km ≈ 2.5 miles
  b 12 km ≈ 7.5 miles
  c 20 km ≈ 12.5 miles
  d 4 miles ≈ 6.4 km

Challenge

a Bill drove 600 km, Frances drove 200 km, Jack drove 320 km and Betty drove 80 km.
b 1200 km = 750 miles

Week 10, Lesson 5 – Pages 94 and 95

Practice

1 a 47.72 km   **b** 95.44 km
2 a 420 cm   **b** 5.8 m
3 a 196 cm   **b** 1.96 m
4 a 6 pairs   **b** 1 metre
5 True

Refresher

1 a Alex is 0.19 m taller than Bob
  b Alex is 0.05 m taller than Chris
  c Derek is 0.07 m taller than Alex
  d Alex is 0.48 m taller than Ellen
2 55 cm
3 Chris

Challenge

1 a

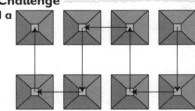

  b 290 m
2 450 m

Week 11, Lesson 1 – Pages 96 and 97

Practice

1 a 8000 − 2994 = 5006
  b 7006 − 3993 = 3013
  c 9008 − 5991 = 3017
  d 6012 − 1989 = 4023
  e 5015 − 2987 = 2028
  f 9000 − 4978 = 4022
  g 8005 − 992 = 7013
  h 6014 − 1978 = 4036

i $7001 - 6975 = 26$
j $10\,000 - 8997 = 1003$
2a $486 + 94 = 580$
 b $797 - 196 = 601$
 c $301 + 594 = 895$
 d $516 + 602 = 1118$
 e $1429 - 499 = 930$
 f $2672 - 503 = 2169$
 g $5810 + 607 = 6417$
 h $9012 - 1395 = 7617$
 i $6375 + 1599 = 7974$
 j $7587 - 1998 = 5589$
3a $6.8 + 1.9 = 8.7$
 b $5.3 - 2.1 = 3.2$
 c $2.3 + 3.1 = 5.4$
 d $5.6 + 2.9 = 8.5$
 e $10.3 - 4.1 = 6.2$
 f $6.7 + 3.9 = 10.6$
 g $8.3 + 5.1 = 13.4$
 h $9.8 - 4.9 = 4.9$
 i $3.6 + 8.1 = 11.7$
 j $7.5 - 1.1 = 6.4$
4a $586 + 297 = 883$
 b $784 + 406 = 1190$
 c $219 + 513 = 732$
 d $651 + 286 = 937$
 e $784 + 173 = 957$
 f $612 + 850 = 1462$
 g $973 + 462 = 1435$
 h $481 + 554 = 1035$
 i $375 + 902 = 1277$
 j $657 + 812 = 1469$

Refresher

1a $286 + 163 = 449$
  $200 + 100 = 300$
  $80 + 60 = 140$
  $6 + 3 = 9$
 b $315 + 206 = 521$
 c $172 + 197 = 369$
 d $368 + 508 = 876$
 e $291 + 265 = 556$
 f $406 + 372 = 778$
 g $472 + 337 = 809$
 h $554 + 256 = 810$
 i $583 + 242 = 825$

j $675 + 185 = 860$
2a $203 - 95 = 108$

 b $506 - 296 = 210$
 c $701 - 394 = 307$
 d $600 - 295 = 305$
 e $504 - 196 = 308$
 f $307 - 99 = 208$
 g $801 - 591 = 210$
 h $906 - 498 = 408$
 i $800 - 296 = 504$
 j $507 - 199 = 308$
3a $286 + 98 = 384$
  $286 + 100 = 386$
  $386 - 2 = 384$
 b $412 - 89 = 323$
 c $352 + 95 = 447$
 d $563 - 194 = 369$
 e $484 + 199 = 683$
 f $561 - 201 = 360$
 g $376 + 104 = 480$
 h $567 - 205 = 362$
 i $491 + 304 = 795$
 j $673 - 202 = 471$

Challenge

Answers will vary

Week 11, Lesson 2 – Pages 98 and 99

Practice

1a 19623
   + 765
   20388
 b $58721 + 491 = 59212$
 c $67529 + 780 = 68309$
 d $56721 + 563 = 57284$
 e $48935 + 609 = 49544$
 f $34627 + 721 = 35348$
 g $80941 + 586 = 81527$
 h $61824 + 638 = 62462$
 i $57638 + 279 = 57917$
 j $73706 + 973 = 74679$

Collins Primary Maths

2a 16724
  $+ 5138$
  21862

b 26849 + 2816 = 29665

c 59371 + 3499 = 62870

d 29726 + 6081 = 35807

e 35862 + 7729 = 43591

f 73892 + 5637 = 79529

g 63715 + 5273 = 68988

h 91863 + 6415 = 98278

i 55985 + 9073 = 65058

j 48212 + 1976 = 50188

3a 407.70
  $+ 58.63$
  466.33

b 512.2 + 97.65 = 609.85

c 267.1 + 98.24 = 365.34

d 365.9 + 78.94 = 444.84

e 683.4 + 95.72 = 779.12

f 987.2 + 58.14 = 1045.34

g 487.5 + 75.73 = 563.23

h 871.9 + 48.72 = 920.62

i 451.4 + 75.91 = 527.31

j 861.7 + 29.67 = 891.37

Refresher

1a 5962
  $+ 307$
  6269

b 7831 + 189 = 8020

c 6214 + 863 = 7077

d 8931 + 749 = 9680

e 4727 + 535 = 5262

f 3861 + 486 = 4347

g 2972 + 408 = 3380

h 6175 + 362 = 6537

i 5096 + 872 = 5968

j 7243 + 574 = 7817

2a 1672
  $+ 2384$
  4056

b 3641 + 5283 = 8924

c 2765 + 2064 = 4829

d 5267 + 5351 = 10618

e 4821 + 3758 = 8579

f 5137 + 4575 = 9712

g 4819 + 2345 = 7164

h 7672 + 1609 = 9281

i 8019 + 3425 = 11444

j 3862 + 4638 = 8500

Challenge

1a 56842
   658
   1473
  $+ 63$
   59036

b 189 + 67 + 84791 + 4862 = 89909

c 95412 + 86 + 3647 + 284 = 99429

d 47 + 5847 + 36568 + 842 = 43304

e 60247 + 2380 + 743 + 95 = 63465

Week 11, Lesson 3 – Pages 100 and 101

Practice

1a 94862
  $- 2394$
  92468

b 38721 − 3282 = 35439

c 97621 − 4265 = 93356

d 73862 − 5135 = 68727

e 59124 − 5305 = 53819

f 48728 − 6809 = 41919

g 72616 − 7234 = 65382

h 63704 − 7617 = 56087

i 49932 − 6341 = 43591

j 51667 − 2571 = 49096

2a 72643
  $- 6249$
  66394

b 58162 − 3714 = 54448

c 64851 − 5206 = 59645

d 96720 − 3167 = 93553

e 53384 − 7192 = 46192

f 86124 − 9517 = 76607

g 73561 − 2874 = 70687

h 25962 − 8175 = 17787

i 32149 − 6072 = 26077

j 49652 − 8572 = 41080

3 a
$$109.70$$
$$-\ 27.36$$
$$\overline{\ \ 82.34}$$
  b $206.3 - 36.21 = 170.09$
  c $591.7 - 61.83 = 529.87$
  d $671.4 - 55.73 = 615.67$
  e $214.6 - 96.28 = 118.32$
  f $585.5 - 73.24 = 512.26$
  g $721.2 - 90.38 = 630.82$
  h $961.8 - 47.29 = 914.51$
  i $638.9 - 47.65 = 591.25$
  j $372.1 - 83.91 = 288.19$
  k $465.6 - 95.31 = 370.29$
  l $392.6 - 41.32 = 351.28$

Refresher

1 a
$$9638$$
$$-\ 481$$
$$\overline{9157}$$
  b $4721 - 652 = 4069$
  c $8672 - 281 = 8391$
  d $5148 - 563 = 4585$
  e $7637 - 271 = 7366$
  f $6249 - 503 = 5746$
  g $9178 - 639 = 8539$
  h $4482 - 721 = 3761$
  i $7963 - 380 = 7583$
  j $8721 - 473 = 8248$

2 a
$$5863$$
$$-\ 2171$$
$$\overline{3692}$$
  b $6973 - 3185 = 3788$
  c $8962 - 4071 = 4891$
  d $5163 - 2945 = 2218$
  e $7948 - 2663 = 5285$
  f $9617 - 3842 = 5775$
  g $7293 - 1637 = 5656$
  h $5541 - 3094 = 2447$
  i $8761 - 3261 = 5500$
  j $6174 - 2536 = 3638$

Challenge

15 calculations

Week 11, Lesson 4 – Pages 102 and 103

Practice

1 a 6 buses hold 312 people
  8 buses hold 416 people
  12 buses hold 624 people
  20 buses hold 1040 people
  b For 126 children they need 3 buses
  For 251 children they need 5 buses
  For 308 children they need 6 buses
  For 467 children they need 9 buses
2 a 4 tickets to York = £225.92
  b 3 tickets to Penzance = £192.54
  c 5 tickets to Manchester = £189.80
  d 1 ticket to York and 1 ticket to Manchester = £94.44
  e 1 ticket to Penzance and 1 ticket to Manchester = £102.14
3 a Leeds to Edinburgh and back = 514 km
  b Cardiff to London to Nottingham = 358 km
  c Leeds to Nottingham to London and back to Nottingham = 403 km
  d London to Nottingham and back = 306 km

Refresher

1 a £2.50 **b** £4.44 **c** £5.22 **d** £3.50
2 a 7 tickets to school
  b 5 tickets to the cinema
  c 5 tickets to the swimming pool
  d 2 tickets to the shopping centre
3 a £4.13 change
  b £3.75 change
  c £8.52 change
  d £1.65 change

Challenge

1 a The first pile has 6 coins, the second pile has 9 coins, the third pile has 12 coins
  b The first pile has 20 coins, the second pile has 11 coins, the third pile has 10 coins
  c The first pile has 8 coins, the second pile has 16 coins, the third pile has 32 coins

Collins Primary Maths

Week 11, Lesson 5 – Pages 104 and 105

Practice

1 a There are 441 children in Keystages 1 and 2

   b There are 31 children per class in Keystage 2

   c There are 520 places in the school in total

   d 7 coaches will be needed

   e £996 will be collected in total

   f 186 children travel by bus

   g 31 children bring packed lunches

   h 83 children were absent

2 Open

Refresher

1 a There are 104 children in Reception and Year 1

   b There are 58 children in Year 2

   c 81 children live less than 500 m from the school

   d 54 children come by car

   e There are 324 gloves

Challenge

1 a Mum weighed 65 kg, Rose weighed 38 kg, Daisy weighed 24 kg

   b Selima will fill 32 buckets. The ratio is 4 : 3.

   c When Theo is on page 72, Luke will be on page 108. It will take Theo 48 days to read the book.

Week 12, Lesson 1 – Pages 106 and 107

Practice

1 a $3^2 = 9$ b $9^2 = 81$

   c $7^2 = 49$ d $4^2 = 16$

   e $12^2 = 144$ f $14^2 = 196$

   g $8^2 = 64$ h $10^2 = 100$

   i $13^2 = 169$ j $6^2 = 36$

   k $5^2 = 25$ l $11^2 = 121$

2 a $2^2 = 4$ b $11^2 = 121$

   c $10^2 = 100$ d $13^2 = 169$

e $7^2 = 49$ f $8^2 = 64$

g $9^2 = 81$ h $12^2 = 144$

3 a $6^2 + 4 = 40$ b $5^2 + 7 = 32$

   c $12^2 + 9 = 153$ d $4^2 - 8 = 8$

   e $8^2 - 12 = 52$ f $11^2 - 18 = 103$

   g $3^2 + 16 = 25$ h $7^2 - 13 = 36$

   i $9^2 + 19 = 100$ j $4^2 + 31 = 47$

   k $5^2 - 19 = 6$ l $7^2 + 18 = 67$

Refresher

1 a $1^2 = 1$ b $3^2 = 9$

   c $5^2 = 25$ d $6^2 = 36$

   e $8^2 = 64$ f $10^2 = 100$

Challenge

1 a $10^2 - 38 = 62$ b $11^2 + 23 = 144$

   c $13^2 - 72 = 97$ d $12^2 - 46 = 98$

   e $9^2 - 55 = 26$ f $8^2 + 37 = 101$

   g $7^2 + 62 = 111$ h $20^2 + 52 = 452$

2 a $4^2 + 3^2 = 25$ b $5^2 + 6^2 = 61$

   c $3^2 + 7^2 = 58$ d $6^2 - 3^2 = 27$

   e $9^2 + 6^2 = 117$ f $8^2 - 5^2 = 39$

   g $10^2 - 7^2 = 51$ h $9^2 - 4^2 = 65$

Week 12, Lesson 2 – Pages 108 and 109

Practice

1

```
                           1
                        1     1
                     1     2     1
                  1     3     3     1
               1     4     6     4     1
            1     5    10    10     5     1
         1     6    15    20    15     6     1
      1     7    21    35    35    21     7     1
   1     8    28    56    70    56    28     8     1
1     9    36    84   126   126    84    36     9     1
1    10    45   120   210   252   210   120    45    10    1
```

2 Answers will vary but should include some, if not all, of the patterns described at 3b.

3 a Answers will vary but should include some, if not all, of the patterns described at 3b.

   b The first diagonal line consists of only 1s. The second diagonal line consists of the ordered natural numbers. The third diagonal line consists of the triangular numbers in sequence, which go odd, odd, even, even, odd, odd … .

The fourth diagonal line consists of numbers whose differences increase consecutively by the natural numbers, starting at 3.

c Use the differences between consecutive numbers

d Row 11 – 55
  Row 12 – 66
  Row 13 – 78
  Row 14 – 91
  Row 15 – 105

The difference between consecutive triangular numbers increases by 1 through the sequence.

Refresher

1 The number of dots on each new row increases by one.

2

Row	Number of dots altogether	Number of dots added
1	1	1
2	3	2
3	6	3
4	10	4
5	15	5

3 a The difference between consecutive triangular numbers increases by 1 through the sequence.

b 13

c They are the number of dots which can be arranged to make successive triangular patterns.

d Yes, 36

e The numbers form the pattern: odd, odd, even, even, odd, odd, even, even ... etc.

Challenge

1 Open

2 512 Each row consists of the same number repeated whose value doubles from one row to the next, going upwards.

Week 12, Lesson 3 – Pages 110 and 111

Practice

1 b

Size of square	Dots outside	Dots inside
1 × 1	8	1
2 × 2	12	4
3 × 3	16	9
4 × 4	20	16
5 × 5	24	25
6 × 6	28	36
7 × 7	32	49
8 × 8	36	64
9 × 9	40	81
10 × 10	44	100

c The number of dots on an outside square is always even and increases by 4 each time. The number of dots on the inside squares relate to the square numbers and so alternate between odd and even. The number of dots on an outside square increases by 4 as the size of an inside square increases by 1.

d The number of dots on an outside square is always a multiple of 4.

Refresher

2 a 100, 104, 108, 112, 116, 120, 124, 128. The rule is + 4.

b 350, 355, 360, 365, 370, 375, 380, 385. The rule is + 5.

c −56, −53, −50, −47, −44, −41, −38, −35. The rule is + 3.

d −33, −22, −11, 0, 11, 22, 33, 44. The rule is + 11.

e 78, 90, 102, 114, 126, 138, 150, 162. The rule is + 12.

f 36, 45, 54, 63, 72, 81, 90, 99. The rule is + 9.

Challenge

The statement is true.

Collins Primary Maths

Week 12, Lesson 4 – Pages 112 and 113

Practice

Answers will vary

Refresher

2a −34, −25, −16, −7, 2, 11, 20, 29, 38, 47. Rule: + 9

b 15, 40, 65, 90, 115, 140, 165, 190, 215, 240. Rule: + 25

c 361, 372, 383, 394, 405, 416, 427, 438, 449, 460. Rule: + 11

d 652, 640, 628, 616, 604, 592, 580, 568, 556, 544. Rule: − 12

e −125, −150, −175, −200, −225, −250, −275, −300, −325, −350. Rule: − 25

f −63, −72, −81, −90, −99, −108, −117, −126, −135, −144. Rule: −9

g 36, 48, 60, 72, 84, 96, 108, 120, 132, 144. Rule: + 12

h −90, −75, −60, −45, −30, −15, 0, 15, 30, 45. Rule: + 15

Challenge

1 Add or subtract the same number each time.

2 Add or subtract the same number each time, or add or subtract a changing number.

3 Answers will vary

Week 12, Lesson 5 – Pages 114 and 115

Practice

1 Table □ = 1 times table
Table △ = 9 times table
Table ○ = 3 times table
Table ◇ = 6 times table

2 Answers will vary

Refresher

1 A = 4

2 B = 5

3 C = 6

4 D = 6

5 E = 9

6 F = 2

7 G = 2

8 H = 3

9 J = 1

10 K = 10

11 L = 10

12 M = 2, N = 3, or multiples of 2 and 3 by same number

13 P = 8

14 T = 6

Challenge

3 Expensive = 5 + 24 + 16 + 5 + 14 + 19 + 9 + 22 + 5 = 119
Thousand = 20 + 8 + 15 + 21 + 19 + 1 + 14 + 4 = 102
Autumn = 1 + 21 + 20 + 21 + 13 + 14 = 90
Christmas = 3 + 8 + 18 + 9 + 19 + 20 + 13 + 1 + 19 = 110

4 Times = $20 \times 9 \times 13 \times 5 \times 19 = 222\,300$
Summer = $19 \times 21 \times 13 \times 13 \times 5 \times 18 = 6\,068\,790$
Compute = $3 \times 15 \times 13 \times 16 \times 21 \times 20 \times 5 = 19\,656\,000$
Million = $13 \times 9 \times 12 \times 12 \times 9 \times 15 \times 14 = 31\,842\,720$

5 Answers will vary

6 Answers will vary

Pupil Book 2

Spring Term

Week 1, Lesson 1 – Pages 4 and 5

Practice

1 a 2 000 000   **b** 50 000   **c** 400
   d 9   **e** 600 000   **f** 60
   g 7 000 000   **h** 3000   **i** 20 000

2 a two million, six hundred and ninety-five thousand, four hundred and eleven

   b nine million, one hundred and fifty-four thousand, three hundred and sixty-seven

   c four million, two hundred and fifty-nine thousand, four hundred and thirteen

   d two million, five hundred and eighty-seven thousand, four hundred and ninety-nine

   e three million, six hundred and twenty-one thousand, eight hundred and forty-seven

   f one million, eighty-seven thousand, nine hundred and sixty-four

   g seven million, five hundred and thirty-eight thousand, four hundred and twenty-nine

   h six million, three hundred and thirty-three thousand, eight hundred and forty-seven

   i eight million, nine hundred and twenty thousand, four hundred and seventy-three

3

Number	Multiple of 10	Multiple of 100	Multiple of 1000
27 862	27 860	27 900	28 000
96 785	96 790	96 800	97 000
14 538	14 540	14 500	15 000
19 003	19 000	19 000	19 000
75 499	75 500	75 500	75 000
50 273	50 270	50 300	50 000
83 251	83 250	83 300	83 000
31 628	31 630	31 600	32 000
59 725	59 730	59 700	60 000
91 351	91 350	91 400	91 000

4 a $8 \times 10 = 80$
     800
     8000
     80 000
     800 000
     8 000 000
   $8 \div 10 = 0.8$
     0.08
     0.008

b $25 \times 10 = 250$
     2500
     25 000
     250 000
     2 500 000
   $25 \div 10 = 2.5$
     0.25
     0.025

c $84 \times 10 = 840$
     8400
     84 000
     840 000
     8 400 000
   $84 \div 10 = 8.4$
     0.84
     0.084

d $176 \times 10 = 1760$
     17 600
     176 000
     1 760 000
   $176 \div 10 = 17.6$
     1.76
     0.176

e $205 \times 10 = 2050$
     20 500
     205 000
     2 050 000
   $205 \div 10 = 20.5$
     2.05
     0.205

f $382 \times 10 = 3820$
     38 200
     38 2000
     38 20000
   $382 \div 10 = 38.2$
     3.82
     0.382

Refresher

1 a 20 000   **b** 5000
   c 400   **d** 7
   e 80   **f** 30 000
   g 4000   **h** 2
   i 800   **j** 9000

2 a twenty-six thousand

   b seventy-five thousand, six hundred and ninety-three

   c twelve thousand, four hundred and seventy-eight

   d fifty-nine thousand, three hundred and forty-seven

   e forty thousand, six hundred and eighty-seven

   f thirty-six thousand, five hundred and twenty-seven

Collins Primary Maths

g sixty-four thousand, two hundred and eighty-three

h seventy-seven thousand, nine hundred and twelve

i sixty-two thousand, eight hundred and thirty-four

j ninety-nine thousand, four hundred and fifty-eight

3

number	multiple of 10	multiple of 100	multiple of 1000
4687	4690	4700	5000
2951	2950	3000	3000
5486	5490	5500	5000
2177	2180	2200	2000
4876	4880	4900	5000
3501	3500	3500	4000
8752	8750	8800	9000
1297	1300	1300	1000
3868	3870	3900	4000
9277	9280	9300	9000
6534	6530	6500	7000

4 Answers will vary

Challenge

a $0.8 \times 10 = 8$
b $56 \times 1000 = 56\,000$
c $18 \div 1000 = 0.018$
d $72\,000 \div 1000 = 72$
e $7.3 \times 100 = 730$
f $148 \div 1000 = 0.148$
g $128 \times 100 = 12\,800$
h $372 \div 100 = 3.72$
i $470 \times 1000 = 470\,000$
j $7852\,621 \div 1000 = 7852.621$

Week 1, Lesson 2 – Pages 6 – 7

Practice

1 Answers will vary

2a 10	**b** 9	**c** 10	**d** 15
e 9	**f** 16	**g** 26	**h** 11
i 10	**j** 9	**k** 34	**l** 34
m 12	**n** 25	**o** 19	**p** 24

Refresher

1 a $-23, -7, -5, 0, 2, 15$
b $-16, -12, 0, 7, 12, 25$

c $-32, -23, -21, -4, 32, 62$
d $-73, -11, 0, 5, 37, 99$
e $-46, -26, -16, 6, 16, 36$

2a 5	**b** 9	**c** 8	**d** 12	**e** 11
f 8	**g** 8	**h** 12	**i** 18	**j** 3

Challenge

1 a $2 - 51 = -49$ **b** $35 - 47 = -12$
c $12 - 59 = -47$ d $75 - 126 = -51$
e $89 - 99 = -10$ f $-45 + 18 = -27$
g $-56 + 78 = 22$ h $-14 + 89 = 75$
i $-63 + 159 = 96$ j $-37 + 96 = 59$
k $-154 + 84 = -70$ l $-68 + 15 = -53$
m $-167 + 77 = -90$
n $-267 + 148 = -119$
o $-208 + 163 = -45$

Week 1, Lesson 3 – Pages 8 and 9

Practice

1a 24	**b** 19	**c** 11	**d** 25	**e** 21
f 34	**g** 33	**h** 15	**i** 16	**j** 17

2a $9 - 12 = -3$ **b** $6 - 15 = -9$
$\quad -3 + 12 = 9$ $\quad -9 + 15 = 6$
c $8 - 13 = -5$ d $10 - 18 = -8$
$\quad -5 + 13 = 8$ $\quad -8 + 18 = 10$
e $4 - 18 = -14$ f $17 - 25 = -8$
$\quad -14 + 18 = 4$ $\quad -8 + 25 = 17$
g $9 - 20 = -11$ h $7 - 16 = -9$
$\quad -11 + 20 = 9$ $\quad -9 + 16 = 7$
i $3 - 24 = -21$ j $2 - 28 = -26$
$\quad -21 + 24 = 3$ $\quad -26 + 28 = 2$
k $-14 + 5 = -9$ l $-33 + 25 = -8$
$\quad -9 - 5 = -14$ $\quad -8 - 25 = -33$
m $-18 + 20 = 2$ n $-19 + 11 = -8$
$\quad 2 - 20 = -18$ $\quad -8 - 11 = -19$
o $-10 + 15 = 5$ p $-6 + 18 = 12$
$\quad 5 - 15 = -10$ $\quad 12 - 18 = -6$
q $-16 + 19 = 3$ r $-3 + 24 = 21$
$\quad 3 - 19 = -16$ $\quad 21 - 24 = -3$
s $-5 + 27 = 22$ t $-21 + 33 = 12$
$\quad 22 - 27 = -5$ $\quad 12 - 33 = -21$

Refresher

1 a 11 $(-5 + 11 = 6)$ **b** 10 $(-8 + 10 = 2)$
c 10 $(-3 + 10 = 7)$ d 11 $(-6 + 11 = 5)$
e 10 $(-1 + 10 = 9)$ f 5 $(-2 + 5 = 3)$

g 12 $(-4 + 12 = 8)$ **h** 15 $(-9 + 15 = 6)$
i 15 $(-10 + 15 = 5)$ **j** 13 $(-3 + 13 = 10)$
k 7 $(-2 + 7 = 5)$ **l** 14 $(-8 + 14 = 6)$

Challenge

1 1 **2** 2 **3** 3

Week 2, Lesson 1 – Pages 10 and 11

Practice

1 a 66, 90, 108, 156 **b** 73, 105, 153
c 7, 29 **d** 49, 196, 1
e 17, 23, 25 **f** 6, 96, $\frac{2}{3}$
g 84, 504 **h** 8, 104, 180
i 12, 21, 66 **j** 73, 89, 121, 153

2 a 18×25 = eg: $18 \times 5 \times 5$, $9 \times 2 \times 5 \times 5$,
$2 \times 3 \times 3 \times 5 \times 5$, $3 \times 6 \times 5 \times 5$

b 33×15 = eg: $33 \times 5 \times 3$, $11 \times 3 \times 5$
$\times 3$, $11 \times 3 \times 15$, $11 \times 9 \times 5$

c 28×12 = eg: $28 \times 4 \times 3$, $28 \times 6 \times 2$, 7
$\times 4 \times 12$, $7 \times 4 \times 4 \times 3$, $7 \times 4 \times 6 \times 2$

d $800 \div 16$ = eg: $(800 \div 4) \div 4$,
$(40 \div 8) \times 20 \div 2$, $(160 \div 16) \times 5$,
$(80 \div 16) \times 10$

e 24×25 = eg: $24 \times 5 \times 5$, $12 \times 2 \times 5$
$\times 5$, $6 \times 4 \times 5 \times 5$, $25 \times 4 \times 6$

f $420 \div 12$ = eg: $(420 \div 6) \div 2$,
$(70 \div 2) \times (6 \div 6)$, $(42 \div 6) \times$
$(10 \div 2)$, $(420 \div 2) \div 6$

g $390 \div 15$ = eg: $(39 \div 3) \times (10 \div 5)$,
$(390 \div 3) \div 5$, $(390 \div 5) \div 3$,
$(30 \div 15) \times 13$

h 27×14 = eg: $27 \times 7 \times 2$, $9 \times 3 \times 7 \times$
2, $14 \times 9 \times 3$, $14 \times 3 \times 3 \times 3$,

i $98 \div 14$ = eg: $(98 \div 2) \div 7$, $(98 \div 7)$
$\div 2$, $(49 \div 7) \times (2 \div 2)$, $14 \times 7 \div 14$

j 25×16 = eg: $25 \times 4 \times 4$, $25 \times 8 \times 2$,
$16 \times 5 \times 5$, $10 \times 5 \times 8$

Refresher

1 a 1, 3, 5, 15
b 1, 2, 3, 4, 6, 8, 12, 24
c 1, 2, 4, 8, 16
d 1, 2, 4, 8, 16, 32
e 1, 2, 3, 6, 7, 14, 21, 42
f 1, 2, 3, 4, 6, 9, 12, 18, 36
g 1, 2, 4, 5, 10, 20
h 1, 2, 3, 6, 9, 18, 27, 54

i 1, 2, 3, 4, 6, 8, 12, 16, 24, 48
j 1, 2, 4, 8, 16, 32, 64
k 1, 2, 4, 5, 8, 10, 20, 40
l 1, 2, 4, 5, 10, 20, 25, 50, 100

Challenge

1 a $(13 \times 4 \times 2) - 20 = 84$
b $4 \times (9 - 7) + 4 = 12$
c $(30 \div 6) + (5 \times 3) = 20$
d $(7 \times 7) + (9 \times 3) = 76$, $7 \times (7 + 9) \times 3$
$= 336$
e $6 \times (7 + 3) + 6 = 66$
f $(56 - 24) \div 8 = 4$
g $48 + (15 \div 3) + 7 = 60$
h $56 \div (8 + 6) = 4$
i $(47 - 11) \times (12 \div 3) = 144$
j $(6 \times 6) \div (4 + 5) = 4$

2 a $(4 \times 11) + (8 \times 7) = 100$
b $(40 - 15) \times (24 \div 6) = 100$
c $(13 + 7) \times (14 - 9) = 100$
d $(56 \div 2) + (8 \times 9) = 100$
e $(8 \times 8) + (9 \times 4) = 100$
f $(26 + 24) \times (16 \div 8) = 100$
g $(85 + 23) - (32 \div 4)$ 100
h $14 + (6 \times 9) + 32 = 100$
i $5 \times (12 \times 4 - 28) = 100$
j $(28 \times 2 - 31) \times 4 = 100$

Week 2, Lesson 2 – Pages 12 and 13

Practice

1 a $0.46 \rightarrow 0.23$ **b** $0.72 \rightarrow 0.36$
c $0.68 \rightarrow 0.34$ **d** $0.34 \rightarrow 0.17$
e $0.9 \rightarrow 0.45$ **f** $0.52 \rightarrow 0.26$

2 a $0.92 \rightarrow 0.46 \rightarrow 0.23$
b $0.8 \rightarrow 0.4 \rightarrow 0.2$
c $0.56 \rightarrow 0.28 \rightarrow 0.14$
d $0.78 \rightarrow 0.39 \rightarrow 0.195$
e $0.32 \rightarrow 0.16 \rightarrow 0.08$
f $0.84 \rightarrow 0.42 \rightarrow 0.21$

3 a $12.8 \rightarrow 6.4 \rightarrow 3.2$
b $62.4 \rightarrow 31.2 \rightarrow 15.6$
c $48.4 \rightarrow 24.2 \rightarrow 12.1$
d $46 \rightarrow 23 \rightarrow 11.5$
e $32.24 \rightarrow 16.12 \rightarrow 8.06$
f $82 \rightarrow 41 \rightarrow 20.5$

4 a 15.6 → 7.8   **b** 72.4 → 36.2
  c 26.3 → 13.15   **d** 44.5 → 22.25
  e 27.8 → 13.9   **f** 68.7 → 34.35

5 a

  b $36.3 \div 2 = 18.15$
  c $18.24 \div 2 = 9.12$
  d $16.7 \div 2 = 8.35$
  e $28.9 \div 2 = 14.45$
  f $42.1 \div 2 = 21.05$
  g $38.4 \div 2 = 19.2$
  h $62.92 \div 2 = 31.46$
  i $78.56 \div 2 = 39.28$

Refresher

$\frac{1}{2} \times 22 = 11$	$\frac{1}{2} \times 34 = 17$
$\frac{1}{2} \times 38 = 19$	$\frac{1}{2} \times 48 = 24$
$\frac{1}{2} \times 54 = 27$	$\frac{1}{2} \times 56 = 28$
$\frac{1}{2} \times 70 = 35$	$\frac{1}{2} \times 72 = 36$
$\frac{1}{2} \times 86 = 43$	$\frac{1}{2} \times 90 = 45$
$\frac{1}{2} \times 94 = 47$	

Week 2, Lesson 3 – Pages 14 and 15

Practice

1

2 a $56 \times 6 = 336$ **b** $37 \times 9 = 333$
  c $29 \times 7 = 203$ **d** $84 \times 8 = 672$
  e $46 \times 6 = 276$ **f** $72 \times 8 = 576$
  g $63 \times 7 = 441$ **h** $4 \times 95 = 380$
  i $78 \times 4 = 312$ **j** $5 \times 39 = 195$
  k $9 \times 74 = 666$ **l** $93 \times 3 = 279$
  m $8 \times 67 = 536$ **n** $77 \times 8 = 616$

Refresher

1 a $38 \times 6 = (30 \times 6) + (8 \times 6)$
            $= 180 + 48$
            $= 228$
  b $45 \times 7 = 315$ **c** $53 \times 4 = 212$
  d $66 \times 5 = 330$ **e** $87 \times 8 = 696$
  f $73 \times 8 = 584$ **g** $96 \times 4 = 384$
  h $63 \times 9 = 567$ **i** $94 \times 7 = 658$
  j $46 \times 7 = 322$ **k** $57 \times 6 = 342$
  l $83 \times 9 = 747$ **m** $64 \times 8 = 512$

Challenge

1 a $89 \times 5 = 445$ **b** $56 \times 8 = 448$
  c $75 \times 6 = 450$ **d** $76 \times 8 = 608$
  e $67 \times 8 = 536$ **f** $71 \times 9 = 639$

Week 2, Lesson 4 – Pages 16 and 17

Practice

1 a $8 \times 49 = (8 \times 50) - 8$
            $= 400 - 8$
            $= 392$
  b $6 \times 49 = 294$ **c** $17 \times 49 = 833$
  d $13 \times 49 = 637$ **e** $15 \times 49 = 735$
  f $23 \times 49 = 1127$ **g** $35 \times 49 = 1715$
  h $54 \times 49 = 2646$ **i** $48 \times 49 = 2352$
  j $67 \times 49 = 3283$

2 a $9 \times 51 = (9 \times 50) + 9$
            $= 450 + 9$
            $= 459$
  b $14 \times 51 = 714$ **c** $18 \times 51 = 918$
  d $25 \times 51 = 1275$ **e** $27 \times 51 = 1377$
  f $36 \times 51 = 1836$ **g** $39 \times 51 = 1989$
  h $43 \times 51 = 2193$ **i** $52 \times 51 = 2652$
  j $68 \times 51 = 3468$

Refresher

  a $36 \times 50 = 1800$ **b** $14 \times 50 = 700$
  c $23 \times 50 = 1150$ **d** $40 \times 50 = 2000$
  e $28 \times 50 = 1400$ **f** $19 \times 50 = 950$
  g $47 \times 50 = 2350$ **h** $33 \times 50 = 1650$
  i $42 \times 50 = 2100$ **j** $54 \times 50 = 2700$
  k $68 \times 50 = 3400$ **l** $90 \times 50 = 4500$
  m $76 \times 50 = 3800$ **n** $58 \times 50 = 2900$
  o $65 \times 50 = 3250$ **p** $84 \times 50 = 4200$
  q $82 \times 50 = 4100$ **r** $72 \times 50 = 3600$
  s $96 \times 50 = 4800$ **t** $93 \times 50 = 4650$

Challenge

1 a Shamima: flower £22.44, diamond
  £9.80, plain £6.25
  Joshua: flower £18.36, diamond
  £11.27, plain £3.75
  Ricardo: flower £29.07, diamond
  £16.66
b Shamima: £38.49
  Joshua: £33.38
  Ricardo: £45.73
2 a Ricardo spent the most money
b Difference between Joshua and
  Shamima is £5.11
  Difference between Joshua and
  Ricardo is £12.35
  Difference between Shamima and
  Ricardo is £7.24

Week 2, Lesson 5 – Pages 18 and 19

Practice

1 a $17 \times 9 = (10 \times 9) + (7 \times 9)$
  $= 90 + 63$
  $= 153$

b $17 \times 15 = 255$	**c** $17 \times 6 = 102$
d $17 \times 13 = 221$	**e** $17 \times 16 = 272$
f $17 \times 22 = 374$	**g** $17 \times 25 = 425$
h $17 \times 31 = 527$	**i** $17 \times 28 = 476$
j $17 \times 40 = 680$	**k** $17 \times 50 = 850$
l $17 \times 35 = 595$	

2 a 238   **b** £102   **c** £15.13
d £425   **e** £578   **f** £41.65

Refresher

1 a $7 \times 10 = 70$	**b** $13 \times 10 = 130$
c $19 \times 10 = 190$	**d** $44 \times 10 = 440$
e $48 \times 10 = 480$	**f** $16 \times 10 = 160$
g $25 \times 10 = 250$	**h** $36 \times 10 = 360$
i $52 \times 10 = 520$	**j** $27 \times 10 = 270$
2 a $8 \times 7 = 56$	**b** $14 \times 7 = 98$
c $12 \times 7 = 84$	**d** $35 \times 7 = 245$
e $43 \times 7 = 301$	**f** $46 \times 7 = 322$
g $28 \times 7 = 196$	**h** $29 \times 7 = 203$
i $58 \times 7 = 406$	**j** $39 \times 7 = 273$

Challenge

60	29	26	65
17	52	33	51
38	44	45	12

Week 3, Lesson 1 – Pages 20 and 21

Practice

Enquiry No: 1 Villa cost: £410
  Cost per person: £68.33

Enquiry No: 2 Villa cost: £865
  Cost per person: £96.11

Enquiry No: 3 Villa cost: £750
  Cost per person: £125

Enquiry No: 4 Villa cost: £355
  Cost per person: £118.33

Enquiry No: 5 Villa cost: £515
  Cost per person: £85.83

Enquiry No: 6 Villa cost: £395
  Cost per person: £79

Enquiry No: 7 Villa cost: £865
  Cost per person: £108.13

Enquiry No: 8 Villa cost: £515
  Cost per person: £73.57

Enquiry No: 9 Villa cost: £455
  Cost per person: £75.83

Refresher

1 a $81 \div 9 = 9$	**b** $36 \div 4 = 9$
$45 \div 9 = 5$	$24 \div 4 = 6$
$63 \div 9 = 7$	$16 \div 4 = 4$
$27 \div 9 = 3$	$40 \div 4 = 10$
$72 \div 9 = 8$	$32 \div 4 = 8$
c $14 \div 7 = 2$	**d** $30 \div 6 = 5$
$63 \div 7 = 9$	$42 \div 6 = 7$
$49 \div 7 = 7$	$18 \div 6 = 3$
$21 \div 7 = 3$	$36 \div 6 = 6$
$56 \div 7 = 8$	$54 \div 6 = 9$

Collins Primary Maths

e $24 \div 3 = 8$ f $16 \div 8 = 2$
$21 \div 3 = 7$ $32 \div 8 = 4$
$9 \div 3 = 3$ $72 \div 8 = 9$
$15 \div 3 = 5$ $24 \div 8 = 3$
$27 \div 3 = 9$ $48 \div 8 = 6$

Challenge
Answers will vary

Week 3, Lesson 2 – Pages 22 and 23

Practice
1 Approximations will vary

a $226 \div 3 \approx 240 \div 3 = 80$

```
3) 226
   210      (70 × 3)
   ___
    16
    15      (5 × 3)
   ___
     1
```

Answer = $75\frac{1}{3}$

or

```
      75
3) 226
   210      (70 × 3)
   ___
    16
    15      (5 × 3)
   ___
     1
```

b $378 \div 4 = 94\frac{2}{4}$ or $94\frac{1}{2}$

c $654 \div 9 = 72\frac{6}{9}$ or $72\frac{2}{3}$

d $450 \div 6 = 75$ **e** $389 \div 8 = 48\frac{5}{8}$

f $588 \div 8 = 73\frac{4}{8}$ or $73\frac{1}{2}$

g $685 \div 7 = 97\frac{6}{7}$ **h** $462 \div 5 = 92\frac{2}{5}$

i $392 \div 6 = 65\frac{2}{6}$ or $65\frac{1}{3}$

j $686 \div 8 = 85\frac{6}{8}$ or $85\frac{3}{4}$

k $748 \div 9 = 83\frac{1}{9}$ **l** $536 \div 7 = 76\frac{4}{7}$

Refresher
1 **a** $48 \div 8 = 6$ **b** $63 \div 9 = 7$
c $47 \div 7 = 6$ r5   **d** $34 \div 5 = 6$ r4
e $52 \div 6 = 8$ r4   **f** $38 \div 4 = 9$ r2
g $240 \div 6 = 40$ **h** $350 \div 5 = 70$
i $720 \div 9 = 80$ **j** $320 \div 8 = 40$
k $400 \div 5 = 80$ **l** $600 \div 6 = 100$
m $280 \div 4 = 70$ **n** $210 \div 7 = 30$
o $160 \div 4 = 40$ **p** $240 \div 3 = 80$
q $270 \div 9 = 30$ **r** $480 \div 8 = 60$

Challenge
1 b, d, f, i, l, m, o, p, r, t
2 **b** $762 \div 9 = 84$ r6
  d $458 \div 3 = 152$ r2
  f $351 \div 4 = 87$ r3
  i $452 \div 3 = 150$ r2
  l $786 \div 9 = 87$ r3
m $373 \div 4 = 93$ r1
  o $229 \div 3 = 76$ r1
  p $687 \div 9 = 76$ r3
  r $658 \div 9 = 73$ r1
  t $742 \div 3 = 247$ r1

Week 3, Lesson 3 – Pages 24 and 25

Practice
1 **a** Tomato: 96.4 cm $\div 7 = 13.77$ cm
  b Mint: 56.4 cm $\div 6 = 9.4$ cm
  c Sunflower: 156.7 cm $\div 7 = 22.39$ cm
  d Basil: 37.4 cm $\div 6 = 6.23$ cm
  e Runner bean: 112.6 cm $\div 8 = 14.08$ cm
  f Parsley: 68.4 cm $\div 6 = 11.4$ cm
  g Potato: 78.3 cm $\div 8 = 9.79$ cm
  h Lavender: 48.4 cm $\div 3 = 16.13$ cm

Refresher
1 Answers will vary

Challenge
a $62.3 \div 7 = 8.9$ **b** $32.0 \div 5 = 6.4$
c $58.5 \div 9 = 6.5$ **d** $30.4 \div 8 = 3.8$
e $34.8 \div 6 = 5.8$ **f** $13.5 \div 3 = 4.5$
g $17.5 \div 7 = 2.5$ **h** $32.4 \div 9 = 3.6$

Week 3, Lesson 4 – Pages 26 and 27

Practice
1

Country	Currency	Exchange rate	Round to nearest whole numbers	£5	£10	£25	£50	£100
Australia	dollars	2.38	2	10	20	50	100	200
India	rupees	60.25	61	305	610	1525	3050	6100
Norway	kroner	12.62	13	65	130	325	650	1300
Mexico	nuevo peso	13.67	14	70	140	350	700	1400
Israel	shekels	5.75	6	30	60	150	300	600
Japan	yen	156.96	157	785	1570	3925	7850	15700

2 **a** £50   **b** £17.50   **c** £4.50   **d** £3.50
  e £8.30   **f** £20   **g** £27.67   **h** £12

Refresher

1 $2 \times £756 \rightarrow 1512$
$2 \times £567 \rightarrow 1134$
$1 \times £189 \rightarrow 189$
$\overline{£2835}$
$4 \times £20 \rightarrow 80$
$1 \times £10 \rightarrow 10$
$\underline{95}$
$\overline{£3020}$

Challenge

Answers will vary

Week 3 Lesson 5 – Pages 28 and 29

Practice

1 a Single to New York = £92
Single to Florida = £123.50
Single to Toronto = £132.50
Single to Los Angeles = £133.50
 b £83
 c $£367 - £184 = £183$
$£183 \div 3 = £61$ per night
2 a £152
 b Single to Dubai = £127.50
Single to Bangkok = £169.50
Single to Hong Kong = £184
Single to Singapore = £203.50
 c $£594 - £339 = £255$
$£255 \div 8 = £31.88$ per night
3 a £188.20   b £47.05, £141.15
4 a £28
 b Child fare to Sydney = £351.75
Child fare to Auckland = £394.50
Child fare to Perth = £420
Child fare to Melbourne = £424.50
 c $(£560 \times 2) + (£420 \times 2) = £1120 + £840 = £1960$

Refresher

1 New York £184   Florida £247
Dubai £255   Toronto £265
Los Angeles £267 Jo'burg £296
Bangkok £339   Cape Town £352
Nairobi £354   Hong Kong £368
Singapore £407   Sydney £469
Durban £514   Auckland £526

Perth £560   Melbourne £566
2 $£566 - £184 = £382$
3 a £795 b £1104 c £1056 d £1578
4 a £1104 b £2442 c £2124 d £2814

Challenge

1 London to: Los Angeles = £279
New York = £239
Nairobi = £377
Jo'Burg = £324
Perth = £548
Sydney = $\underline{£465}$
Total £2232
Round the World Fare $\underline{- £849}$
Difference $\overline{£1383}$
2 50% of £2232   £1116
Round the World Fare $\underline{- £849}$
$\overline{£267}$

Round the World Fare is cheaper by £267.

Week 4, Lesson 1 – Pages 30 and 31

Practice

1 a $\frac{1}{2}, \frac{2}{3}, \frac{5}{6}$ b $\frac{2}{5}, \frac{6}{10}, \frac{3}{4}$ c $\frac{3}{16}, \frac{2}{8}, \frac{3}{4}$
 d $\frac{1}{6}, \frac{2}{9}, \frac{1}{3}$ e $\frac{2}{7}, \frac{1}{3}, \frac{5}{7}$ f $\frac{1}{5}, \frac{3}{10}, \frac{2}{3}$
 g $\frac{3}{4}, \frac{4}{5}, \frac{9}{10}$ h $\frac{2}{6}, \frac{3}{8}, \frac{1}{2}$ i $\frac{1}{3}, \frac{2}{3}, \frac{5}{7}$
 j $\frac{7}{12}, \frac{4}{6}, \frac{3}{4}$ k $\frac{1}{4}, \frac{2}{6}, \frac{2}{3}$ l $\frac{5}{8}, \frac{3}{4}, \frac{13}{16}$
 m $\frac{2}{3}, \frac{7}{9}, \frac{5}{6}$ n $\frac{2}{5}, \frac{7}{10}, \frac{3}{4}$ o $\frac{2}{6}, \frac{2}{5}, \frac{5}{10}$
 p $\frac{1}{2}, \frac{4}{6}, \frac{7}{9}$ q $\frac{5}{9}, \frac{2}{3}, \frac{3}{4}$ r $\frac{1}{3}, \frac{6}{8}, \frac{20}{24}$
 s $\frac{1}{9}, \frac{5}{18}, \frac{2}{6}$ t $\frac{1}{2}, \frac{5}{7}, \frac{3}{4}$

Refresher

1 a $\frac{5}{10}, \frac{6}{10}$ b $\frac{4}{8}, \frac{6}{8}$ c $\frac{3}{6}, \frac{4}{6}$
 d $\frac{10}{15}, \frac{12}{15}$ e $\frac{6}{12}, \frac{9}{12}$ f $\frac{5}{20}, \frac{16}{20}$
2 a $\frac{8}{12}, \frac{3}{12}$ b $\frac{15}{20}, \frac{14}{20}$ c $\frac{3}{6}, \frac{2}{6}$ d $\frac{5}{20}, \frac{8}{20}$
 e $\frac{10}{15}, \frac{6}{15}$ f $\frac{12}{18}, \frac{10}{18}$ g $\frac{15}{24}, \frac{16}{24}$

Challenge

1

$2\frac{27}{60}$ or $2\frac{9}{20}$

$\frac{17}{12}$	$\frac{62}{60}$	
$\frac{5}{6}$	$\frac{7}{12}$	$\frac{9}{20}$

$\frac{1}{2}$	$\frac{1}{3}$	$\frac{1}{4}$	$\frac{1}{5}$

Collins Primary Maths

2

$1\frac{14}{30}$ or $1\frac{7}{15}$			
$\frac{9}{10}$		$\frac{17}{30}$	
$\frac{6}{10}$	$\frac{3}{10}$		$\frac{4}{15}$
$\frac{1}{2}$	$\frac{1}{10}$	$\frac{1}{5}$	$\frac{1}{15}$

Week 4, Lesson 2 – Pages 32 and 33

Practice

1 a 24, £15, 36

b 1380, 1196, £690

c 500, 100 km, 7.5 m

d $38\frac{1}{4}$ or 38.25, 675, $199\frac{1}{2}$ or 199.5

e 112, 28, 800 m

f 160, £34, 220

g 328, $9\frac{3}{5}$ or 9.6 m, 880

h $3\frac{3}{5}$ or 3.6 m, 240, 30 p

i $10\frac{1}{3}$ or 10.33, 1280, £32

j £531.25, 1005, 370

Refresher

1 a $\frac{1}{4}$ of 440 = 110 (440 ÷ 4 = 110)

b 180

c 104

d 24

e 24 (96 ÷ 4), 72 (24 × 3)

f 50, 150

g 10, 50

h 16, 64

i 4, 28

j 6, 36

k 2000, 6000

l 206, 412

Challenge

1 a 60 cm   **b** 920 g   **c** 7 mm

d 350 cm   **e** 3850 ml

Week 4, Lesson 3 – Pages 34 and 35

Practice

1

whole number	tenths	number	tenths	whole number
4	4.6	4.63	4.7	5
7	7.9	7.92	8.0	8
3	3.4	3.49	3.5	4
0	0.5	0.51	0.6	1
8	8.7	8.75	8.8	9
9	9.1	9.16	9.2	10
22	22.0	22.06	22.1	23
45	45.9	45.99	46.0	46
31	31.3	31.39	31.4	32
17	17.2	17.28	17.3	18
34	34.7	34.72	34.8	35
58	58.5	58.51	58.6	59

2 a 5.2, 5.23, 5.32, 5.36, 5.6, 5.61

b 7.066, 7.66, 7.68, 7.8, 7.86, 7.866

c 2.001, 2.021, 2.2, 2.202, 2.21, 2.211

d 9.5, 9.57, 9.571, 9.7, 9.75, 9.771

e 12.4, 12.46, 12.64, 21.4, 21.401, 21.406

f 47.005, 47.015, 47.05, 47.15, 47.475, 47.5

g 84.1, 84.114, 84.14, 84.4, 84.41, 84.441

h 66.6, 66.696, 66.9, 66.96, 66.99, 66.996

i 0.2, 0.21, 0.224, 0.4, 0.412, 0.42

j 15.02, 15.026, 15.226, 15.26, 15.262, 15.6

Refresher

1 a 4 4.8 <u>5</u>   **b** 5 5.6 <u>6</u>

c <u>2</u> 2.3 3   **d** 1 1.7 <u>2</u>

e <u>9</u> 9.2 10   **f** 4 4.56 <u>5</u>

g 9 9.7 <u>10</u>   **h** 3 3.98 <u>4</u>

i <u>7</u> 7.49 8   **j** 6 6.52 <u>7</u>

2 a 8.1, 8.2, 8.3, 8.6, 8.7, 8.9

b 2.06, 2.12, 2.26, 2.45, 2.78, 2.95

c 5.02, 5.06, 5.22, 5.26, 5.62, 5.66

d 7.07, 7.49, 7.69, 7.94, 7.96, 7.99

e 3.03, 3.06, 3.13, 3.31, 3.36, 3.63

f 9.15, 9.5, 9.56, 9.6, 9.67, 9.7

g 2.14, 2.59, 2.6, 2.8, 2.87, 2.9

h 4.4, 4.47, 4.7, 4.74, 4.77, 4.89

i 6.1, 6.4, 6.51, 6.73, 6.82, 6.9

j 12.48, 12.5, 12.63, 12.77, 12.8, 12.81

Challenge

1 3.6	2 7.37
3 9.91	4 4.991
5 13.449	

Week 4, Lesson 4 – Pages 36 and 37

Practice

1 a

fraction	equivalent decimal	calculation
$\frac{3}{4}$	0.75	$(1 \div 4) \times 3$
$\frac{2}{5}$	0.4	$(1 \div 5) \times 2$
$\frac{1}{3}$	0.333	$1 \div 3$
$\frac{1}{8}$	0.125	$1 \div 8$
$\frac{4}{8}$	0.5	$(1 \div 8) \times 4$
$\frac{4}{10}$	0.4	$(1 \div 10) \times 4$
$\frac{2}{3}$	0.666	$(1 \div 3) \times 2$
$\frac{4}{5}$	0.8	$(1 \div 5) \times 4$
$\frac{7}{8}$	0.875	$(1 \div 8) \times 7$

b

fraction	equivalent %	calculation
$\frac{3}{4}$	75%	$(100 \div 4) \times 3$
$\frac{2}{5}$	40%	$(100 \div 5) \times 2$
$\frac{1}{3}$	33.3%	$(100 \div 3) \times 1$
$\frac{1}{8}$	12.5%	$(100 \div 8) \times 1$
$\frac{4}{8}$	50%	$(100 \div 8) \times 4$
$\frac{4}{10}$	40%	$(100 \div 10) \times 4$
$\frac{2}{3}$	66.6%	$(100 \div 3) \times 2$
$\frac{4}{5}$	80%	$(100 \div 5) \times 4$
$\frac{7}{8}$	87.5%	$(100 \div 8) \times 7$

2 The terms 'fraction', 'decimal' and 'percentage' all mean 'part of the whole of something'. Any fraction can be expressed as a decimal by dividing its denominator into its numerator. In percentage, the whole of something is represented by 100%. So, any percentage can be expressed by a fraction whose denominator is 100, or by a decimal obtained by dividing the numerator by 100.

Refresher

1 a 0.5	b 0.25	c 0.2
d 0.125	e 0.1	f 0.01

2 a 50%	b 25%	c 20%
d $12\frac{1}{2}$ %	e 10%	f 1%
3 a 0.5	b 0.4	c 0.36
d 0.75	e 0.8	
4 a 50%	b 40%	c 36%
d 75%	e 80%	

Challenge

1 a 0.1111, 11.11%	b 0.0909, 9.09%
c 0.0833, 8.33%	d 0.1429, 14.29%
e 0.0667, 6.67%	

Week 4, Lesson 5 – Pages 38 and 39

Practice

1

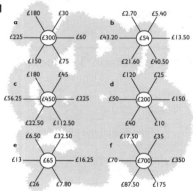

Refresher

1 a £400, £200	b £12, £6
c £310, £155	d £23, £11.50
e £7, £14	f £14, £28
g £30, £60	h £2, £8
i £48, £192	j £1.20, £4.80

Challenge

1 a £7	b £13.13	c £2.63
d £15.05	e £5.60	

Week 5, Lesson 1 – Pages 40 and 41

Practice
Open

Refresher
Open

 Collins Primary Maths

Challenge

Open

Week 5, Lesson 2 – Pages 42 and 43

Practice

Open

Refresher

1 a Region 1: pentagonal pyramid
   Region 2: tetrahedron
   Region 3: cube, octahedron
 b Region 1: dodecahedron, cuboid
   Region 2: triangular prism
   Region 3: square-based pyramid

Challenge

Open

Week 5, Lesson 3 – Pages 44 and 45

Practice

2

shape	✓	✗
a	✓	
b	✓	
c	✓	
d	✓	
e	✓	
f	✓	
g	✓	
h	✓	
i	✓	
j	✓	
k	✓	
l		✗

3 7

Refresher

1

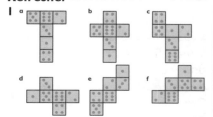

Challenge

1 $3 \times 3 \times 3$ cube
   0 blue faces = 1
   1 blue face = 6
   2 blue faces = 12
   3 blue faces = 8
   4 blue faces = 0

2 $4 \times 4 \times 4$ cube $5 \times 5 \times 5$ cube
   0 blue faces = 8   0 blue faces = 27
   1 blue face = 24   1 blue face = 54
   2 blue faces = 24   2 blue faces = 36
   3 blue faces = 8   3 blue faces = 8
   4 blue faces = 0   4 blue faces = 0

Week 5, Lesson 4 – Pages 46 and 47

Practice

2   a   b   c

3

Refresher

1   a   b   c

2   a   b

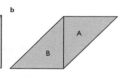

Week 5, Lesson 5 – Pages 48 and 49

Practice

1   a   b

2

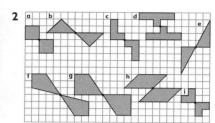

3a

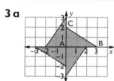

b (3,0), (0, −3), (−3, 0), (0, 3)

4 A (2, 4), C (4, −2), E (−2, −4), G (−4, 2)

Refresher

1 Open

Challenge

1

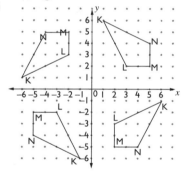

2

vertex	quadrant			
	1st	2nd	3rd	4th
K	(1, 6)	(−6, 1)	(−1, −6)	(6, −1)
L	(3, 2)	(−2, 3)	(−3, −2)	(2, −3)
M	(5, 2)	(−2, 5)	(−5, −2)	(2, −5)
N	(5, 4)	(−4, 5)	(−5, −4)	(4, −5)

3 Each vertex has the same pair of numbers as coordinates, which switch places and change signs with each turn of the triangle.

Week 6, Lesson 1 — Pages 50 and 51

Practice

1 Skier A: 40°, 25°, 103°, 107°, 77°
Skier B: 28°, 54°, 140°, 76°, 128°

2a 72° + 80° + 28° = 180°

b 40° + 73° + 67° = 180°

Refresher

1a 60°	**b** 140°	**c** 30°	**d** 70°
e 45°	**f** 135°	**g** 135°	**h** 25°
i 155°	**j** 135°	**k** 90°	**l** 90°

Challenge

1 d The four triangles have equal angles and equal sides (congruent).

2 The four triangles should be congruent.

Week 6, Lesson 2 — Pages 52 and 53

Practice

1

acute	right	obtuse	straight	reflex
75°	90°	157°	180°	205°
36°		134°		190°
				340°
				275°

4a Angle C = 75°   **b** Angle R = 66°

Refresher

1a 135°   **b** 135°   **c** 225°

2a South   **b** South-west

c North-east   **d** North-west

e East

Challenge

1 Answers will vary

3 The angle subtended by the diameter of a semi-circle at its circumference is always 90°.

Week 6, Lesson 3 — Pages 54 and 55

Practice

1a S = 40°, T = 105°

b Sum of S and T = 145°

2a A = 45°, B = 65°, C = 70°

b A + B + C = 180°

Collins Primary Maths

3 a A = 53°, B = 61°
  b C = 88°, D = 88°
  c E = 33°, F = 52°
4 a Reflex, 316°   **b** Obtuse, 112°
  c Obtuse, 140°   **d** Obtuse, 110°

Refresher
1 a 30°, 90°, 60°
  b 60°, 120°, 60°
  c 90°, 60°, 120°, 120°
2 a A = 270°, B = 310°, C = 125°,
   D = 332°, E = 337°, F = 116°

Challenge
1 Open
2 Open

Week 6, Lesson 4 – Pages 56 and 57

Practice
1 a 52 cm^2 **b** 80 cm^2 **c** 128 cm^2
  d 116 cm^2 **e** 112 cm^2
2 a 215 cm^2 **b** 290 cm^2
  c 162 cm^2 **d** 175 cm^2

Refresher
1 a 6 cm^2 **b** 9 cm^2 **c** 8 cm^2
  d 10 cm^2 **e** 19 cm^2 **f** 16 cm^2

Challenge
2

	cube 1	cube 2	cube 3	cube 4
surface area of one face	4 cm^2	9 cm^2	16 cm^2	25 cm^2
surface area of cube	24 cm^2	54 cm^2	96 cm^2	150 cm^2

3 Pattern: $6 \times (side)^2$
  10 cm cube: 600 cm^2
  15 cm cube: 1350 cm^2
  50 cm cube: 15 000 cm^2
4 a 78 cm^2 **b** 280 cm^2

Week 6, Lesson 5 – Pages 58 and 59

Practice
1 a 8 cm^2 **b** 2 cm^2 **c** 18 cm^2
  d 40.5 cm^2 **e** 50 cm^2 **f** 60.5 cm^2
2 A = 4.5 cm^2
  B = 12.5 cm^2
  C = 24.5 cm^2

3 144 cm^2
4 a A + B = 72 cm^2 **b** A = 36 cm^2
  c C = 9 cm^2 **d** G = 18 cm^2
  e F = 18 cm^2

Refresher
1 Open
2 Open

Challenge
1

N° pins inside	0	1	2	3	4	5
Area in cm^2	3	4	5	6	7	8

2 Area = Number of pins inside + 3
  6 pins inside: area = 9 cm^2
  10 pins inside: area = 13 cm^2

Week 7, Lesson 1 – Pages 60 and 61

Practice
1 a 20 cm^2 **b** 24 cm^2 **c** 16 cm^2
  d 25 cm^2 **e** 24.5 cm^2 **f** 36 cm^2
2 c 12 cm^2, 9 cm^2, 10 cm^2, 12.5 cm^2
3 Open

Refresher
1 a 4 cm^2 **b** 6 cm^2 **c** 4.5 cm^2
  d 6 cm^2 **e** 8 cm^2 **f** 8 cm^2
2 a Triangle d has the same area as
   triangle b.
  b Triangle f has the same area as
   triangle e.

Challenge
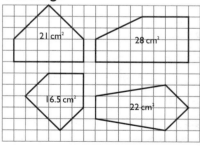

Week 7, Lesson 2 – Pages 62 and 63

Practice

1

weight	rounded to nearest $\frac{1}{10}$ kg	rounded to nearest kg
83.635 kg	83.6	84
a 46.270 kg	46.3	46
b 67.475 kg	67.5	67
c 59.520 kg	59.5	60
d 70.090 kg	70.1	70
e 112.875 kg	112.9	113
f 111.040 kg	111.0	111
g 94.760 kg	94.8	95

2

	whale	tonnes	kilograms
a	blue whale	150	150 000
b	sei whale	20	20 000
c	humpback whale	25	25 000
d	killer whale (male)	9	9000
e	killer whale (female)	6.4	6400
f	narwhal	1.5	1500
g	minke whale	8	8000
h	sperm whale	57	57 000
i	pygmy sperm whale	0.4	400
j	dwarf sperm whale	0.21	210

3 a Blue whale is 6 times heavier.
 b Blue whale is 100 times heavier.
 c Blue whale is 375 times heavier.

Refresher

1 a 0.3 kg, 0.03 kg, 0.003 kg
 b 0.6 kg, 0.06 kg, 0.006 kg
2 a $\frac{9}{10}$ kg, $\frac{9}{100}$ kg, $\frac{9}{1000}$ kg
 b $\frac{7}{10}$ kg, $\frac{7}{100}$ kg, $\frac{7}{1000}$ kg

3

plastic pen caps	weight
1000	1 kg or 1·0 kg
100	$\frac{1}{10}$ kg or 0.1 kg
10	$\frac{1}{100}$ kg or 0·01 kg
1	$\frac{1}{1000}$ or 0·001 kg

Challenge

1 a 4000 kg   **b** 40 000 kg
2 20 000 times larger
3 6 tonnes or 6000 kg

Week 7, Lesson 3 – Pages 64 and 65

Practice

1 Meera: 800 g   Tom: 8 g
 Jenny: 80 g   Sam: 8000 g

2

Backpack	Rounded to nearest $\frac{1}{10}$ kg	Rounded to nearest kg
Delroy	5.2	5
Meera	5.8	6
Tom	6.5	6
Jenny	4.7	5
Sam	8.2	8
Amy	7.6	8

3 a 1230 g **b** 2344 g **c** 2904 g **d** 3472 g

Refresher

1 a 5 kg 248 g, 5 kg 813 g, 6 kg 478 g, 4 kg
   685 g, 8 kg 157 g, 7 kg 589 g
 b 5248 g, 5813 g, 6478 g, 4685 g,
   8157 g, 7589 g
2 5.813 kg → 1 g × 3
        10 g × 1
        100 g × 8
        1000 g × 5

   6.478 kg → 1 g × 8
        10 g × 7
        100 g × 4
        1000 g × 6

   4.685 kg → 1 g × 5
        10 g × 8
        100 g × 6
        1000 g × 4

   8.157 kg → 1 g × 7
        10 g × 5
        100 g × 1
        1000 g × 8

   7.589 kg → 1 g × 9
        10 g × 8
        100 g × 5
        1000 g × 7

Challenge

1 Delroy + Meera + Jenny = Sam + Amy
 (5.248 + 5.813 + 4.685) kg = (8.157 +
 7.589) kg
2 Amy will give Jenny 1452 g

Week 8, Lesson 1 – Pages 66 and 67

Practice

1 $\frac{1}{2}$ lb ≈ 227 g $\frac{1}{4}$ lb ≈ 113.5 g
   $\frac{3}{4}$ lb ≈ 340.5 g

45

 Collins Primary Maths

2 a 200 g   **b** 1 oz   **c** 400 g
    d 900 g   **e** 9 oz   **f** 13 oz

3

Item	Metric	Imperial
cornflakes	500 g	18 oz
marmalade	340 g	12 oz
butter	200 g	7 oz
tin of tuna	90 g	3 oz
tea	114 g	$\frac{1}{4}$ lb
bread	795 g	$1\frac{3}{4}$ lb

4 3 balls

Refresher

1 a 4 oz, 8 oz, 12 oz
   b 4 oz, 8 oz, 12 oz
2 a True   **b** True   **c** False   **d** True
   e True   **f** False   **g** True   **h** False

Challenge

   a $(1 + 2 + 8)$ oz
   b $(1 + 2 + 4 + 8)$ oz
   c $(1 + 2 + 4 + 16)$ oz
   d $(2 + 4 + 8 + 16)$ oz
   e $(1 + 2 + 8 + 32)$ oz
   f $(1 + 2 + 4 + 8 + 32)$ oz
   g $(1 + 2 + 4 + 16 + 32)$ oz
   h $(2 + 4 + 8 + 16 + 32)$ oz
   i $(2 + 4 + 64)$ oz

Week 8, Lesson 2 – Pages 68 and 69

Practice

1

	Total in kg
	$2.1 + 0.5 = 2.6$
a	$1.8 + 0.4 = 2.2$
b	$1.62 + 0.5 = 2.12$
c	$3.3 + 0.5 = 3.8$
d	$3.72 + 0.4 = 4.12$
e	$3.3 + 0.5 = 3.8$

2 7 copies
3 a 10 customers   **b** 13.3 kg

Refresher

1

Newspaper	Weight	Newsagent 1 Copies	Newsagent 1 Weight	Newsagent 2 Copies	Newsagent 2 Weight
Daily Times	270 g	20	5·4 kg	30	8·1 kg
Herald	300 g	50	15·0 kg	75	22·5 kg
Morning Express	350 g	30	10·5 kg	50	17·5 kg
Daily News	250 g	60	15·0 kg	40	10·0 kg
		Total weight	45·9 kg	Total weight	58·1 kg

2 12.2 kg

Challenge

1 Kenny's bag = 6.6 kg, Liam's bag = 7.2 kg, Mike's bag = 7.2 kg
2 Open

Week 8, Lesson 3 – Pages 70 and 71

Practice

1
   $0 \times 6 = 0$ $1 \times 6 = 6$
   $2 \times 6 = 12$ $3 \times 6 = 18$
   $4 \times 6 = 24$ $5 \times 6 = 30$
   $6 \times 6 = 36$ $7 \times 6 = 42$
   $8 \times 6 = 48$ $9 \times 6 = 54$
   $10 \times 6 = 60$

2

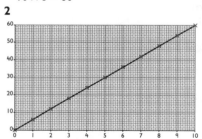

3 a $1\frac{1}{2} \times 6 = 9$ **b** $8\frac{1}{2} \times 6 = 51$
   c $4\frac{1}{2} \times 6 = 27$ **d** $3.5 \times 6 = 21$
   e $9.5 \times 6 = 57$ **f** $7.5 \times 6 = 45$
   g $54 \div 6 = 9$ **h** $33 \div 6 = 5\frac{1}{2}$
   i $15 \div 6 = 2\frac{1}{2}$

4 a 63 p   **b** £1.02   **c** 81 p
   d 75 p   **e** £1.83

Refresher

1
   $0 \times 4 = 0$ $1 \times 4 = 4$
   $2 \times 4 = 8$ $3 \times 4 = 12$
   $4 \times 4 = 16$ $5 \times 4 = 20$
   $6 \times 4 = 24$ $7 \times 4 = 28$
   $8 \times 4 = 32$ $9 \times 4 = 36$
   $10 \times 4 = 40$

2

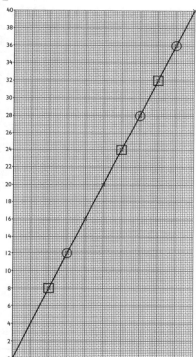

Challenge
1

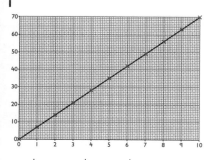

2a $1\frac{1}{2} \times 7 = 10\frac{1}{2}$ **b** $8\frac{1}{2} \times 7 = 59.5$
c $4\frac{1}{2} \times 7 = 31\frac{1}{2}$ **d** $3.5 \times 7 = 24.5$
e $9.6 \times 7 = 67.2$ **f** $7.2 \times 6 = 43.2$

3a $40 \div 7 = 5.7$
 b $52 \div 7 = 7.4$
 c $19 \div 7 = 2.7$

4a £38.50   **b** £105.70   **c** £80.50

Week 8, Lesson 4 – Pages 72 and 73

Practice
1 a 20 minutes
  b 23 minutes
  c 50 minutes
2a 10 miles   **b** 40 miles   **c** 24 miles
3

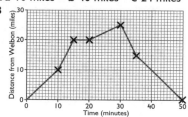

4a 5 minutes   **b** 11 minutes
5a 22.5 miles   **b** 14 miles

Refresher
1

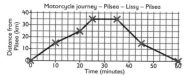

2a 20 km   **b** 35 km   **c** 25 km   **d** 5 km

Challenge
1

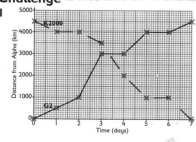

Week 8, Lesson 5 – Pages 74 and 75

Practice
1 a 27 litres   **b** 63 litres
  c 22 litres   **d** 77 litres

Collins Primary Maths

2 a 20 gallons   **b** 6.5 gallons
  c 15.5 gallons   **d** 4 gallons

3

Gallons	Litres (l)
0	0
2	9
4	18
6	27
8	36
10	45

4

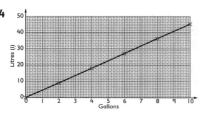

5 a 22.5 litres   **b** 40.5 litres
  c 6 litres   **d** 35 litres
6 a 3.3 gallons   **b** 8.9 gallons
  c 6.2 gallons   **d** 7.6 gallons

Refresher

1

kilograms(kg)	pounds (lb)
0	0
1	2
2	4
3	6
4	8
5	10
6	12
7	14
8	16

2

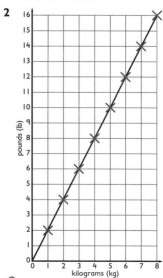

3 a 5 lb   **b** 15 lb   **c** 3 lb   **d** 9 lb
4 a 5.5 kg   **b** 0.5 kg   **c** 6.5 kg   **d** 3.5 kg

Challenge

1

kilograms (kg)	pounds (lb)
0	0
10	22
20	44
30	66
40	88
50	110
60	132
70	154
80	176

2

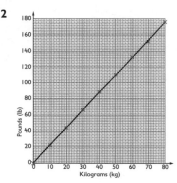

3 a 55 lb   **b** 37 lb   **c** 136 lb   **d** 94 lb
4 a 55 kg   **b** 16.5 kg   **c** 43 kg   **d** 64.5 kg

Week 9, Lesson 1, Pages 76 and 77

Practice

1 a 48 723 + 9614 = 58 337
  b 83 715 + 28 624 = 112 339
  c 72 417 + 3894 = 76 311
  d 63 891 + 2584 = 66 475
  e 75 129 + 58 421 = 133 550
  f 3651 + 82 496 = 86 147
  g 4637 + 81 284 = 85 921
  h 36 527 + 23 945 = 60 472
  i 48 326 + 47 391 = 95 717
  j 59 823 + 14 965 = 74 788
  k 7593 + 24 863 = 32 456
  l 45 381 + 9578 = 54 959
 m 158 496 + 35 821 = 194 317
  n 758 236 + 48 362 = 806 598
  o 163 954 + 478 531 = 642 485
  p 963 158 + 239 647 = 1 202 805
  q 85 136 + 743 085 = 828 221

r $7631 + 813624 = 821255$

s $863247 + 7230 = 870477$

2 a $48632 + 593 + 1578 = 50803$

b $2678 + 3691 + 28749 = 35118$

c $392 + 47695 + 3825 = 51912$

d $48 + 9247 + 63814 = 73109$

e $862 + 3954 + 58432 = 63248$

f $15823 + 3145 + 1587 = 20555$

g $49 + 48762 + 69854 = 118665$

h $85713 + 5482 + 632 = 91827$

i $899 + 3621 + 58472 = 62992$

j $30452 + 6259 + 457 = 37168$

Refresher

1 a $12 + 6 = 18$ **b** $9 + 8 = 17$

c $7 + 4 = 11$ **d** $2 + 13 = 15$

e $15 + 3 = 18$ **f** $8 + 6 = 14$

g $5 + 9 = 14$ **h** $11 + 7 = 18$

i $12 + 8 = 20$ **j** $4 + 8 = 12$

k $13 + 5 = 18$ **l** $7 + 6 = 13$

m $9 + 9 = 18$ **n** $14 + 5 = 19$

o $2 + 16 = 18$ **p** $4 + 15 = 19$

2 a $3642 + 5183 = 8825$

b $5627 + 2649 = 8276$

c $4085 + 5376 = 9461$

d $6243 + 5375 = 11618$

e $9481 + 352 = 9833$

f $8732 + 539 = 9271$

g $76589 + 3072 = 79661$

h $36781 + 2906 = 39687$

i $43374 + 4917 = 48291$

j $52476 + 9153 = 61629$

k $27635 + 45125 = 72760$

l $53962 + 24971 = 78933$

Challenge

1 a $45 + 3687 + 28954 + 487263 =$
519949

b $78541 + 691523 + 48327 + 154 =$
818545

c $759316 + 4829 + 86 + 763 = 764994$

d $9 + 6859 + 793845 + 692 + 785169$
$= 1586574$

e $957824 + 6953 + 482 + 8 + 83174$
$= 1048441$

f $785 + 693184 + 7256 + 7 + 59 =$
701291

g $8079 + 91532 + 73 + 480635 + 631$

$= 580950$

h $385 + 18965 + 8475 + 896584 +$
$709 = 925118$

Week 9, Lesson 2 – Pages 78 and 79

Practice

1 a $15.487 + 32.721 = 48.208$

b $39.47 + 83.29 = 122.76$

c $146.86 + 48.69 = 195.55$

d $4.954 + 15.752 = 20.706$

e $725.63 + 47.15 = 772.78$

f $483.92 + 74.6 = 558.52$

g $4583.9 + 143.92 = 4727.82$

h $692.8 + 63.704 = 756.504$

i $80.437 + 7.71 = 88.147$

j $8.43 + 164.22 = 172.65$

k $6921.5 + 751.78 = 7673.28$

l $7596.4 + 83.15 = 7679.55$

m $752.62 + 4852.32 = 5604.94$

n $9621.4 + 3678.88 = 13300.28$

o $63.781 + 932.7 = 996.481$

p $9.663 + 87.63 = 97.293$

2 a $38.48 + 51.957 + 3.54 = 93.977$

b $7.548 + 36.45 + 7259.4 = 7303.398$

c $721.8 + 36.842 + 3.874 = 762.516$

d $2631.7 + 6.485 + 1.36 = 2639.545$

e $423.84 + 3.801 + 60.771 = 488.412$

f $183.425 + 84.04 + 8.777 = 276.242$

g $71.823 + 614.4 + 8.003 = 694.226$

h $823.14 + 85.744 + 5831.5 = 6740.384$

i $63.75 + 444.8 + 1005.7 = 1514.25$

j $76.14 + 7.88 + 8.152 = 92.172$

k $9002.4 + 71.312 + 8.459 = 9082.171$

l $6.77 + 5.162 + 7824.3 = 7836.232$

m $1963.4 + 853.72 + 74.63 = 2891.75$

n $8.774 + 64.9 + 1532.23 = 1605.904$

o $20.44 + 81.753 + 6073.2 = 6175.393$

p $13.651 + 4.09 + 102.45 = 120.191$

Refresher

1 a $0.4 + 0.6 = 1$ **b** $0.6 + 0.4 = 1$

c $0.1 + 0.9 = 1$ **d** $0.7 + 0.3 = 1$

e $0.9 + 0.1 = 1$ **f** $0.2 + 0.8 = 1$

g $0.5 + 0.5 = 1$ **h** $0.3 + 0.7 = 1$

i $0.8 + 0.2 = 1$

Collins Primary Maths

2 a $5.87 + 36.84 = 42.71$
 b $96.61 + 19.55 = 116.16$
 c $73.47 + 26.61 = 100.08$
 d $85.12 + 48.33 = 133.45$
 e $81.29 + 28.32 = 109.61$
 f $157.6 + 81.7 = 239.3$
 g $395.7 + 42.1 = 437.8$
 h $347.6 + 83.7 = 431.3$
 i $48.7 + 211.3 = 260$
 j $75.2 + 504.4 = 579.6$
 k $2.581 + 85.374 = 87.955$
 l $44.921 + 2.847 = 47.768$
 m $41.951 + 84.267 = 126.218$
 n $2.305 + 43.617 = 45.922$
 o $92.364 + 5.311 = 97.675$

Challenge

1 a $4.896 + 5.7 = 10.596$
 b $8.46 + 57.9 = 66.36$
 c $476.5 + 8.9 = 485.4$
 d $68.59 + 4.7 = 73.29$
 e $4.67 + 8.59 = 13.26$
 f $5.64 + 98.7 = 104.34$

Week 9, Lesson 3 – Pages 80 and 81

Practice

1 a $35245 - 4189 = 31056$
 b $76314 - 8271 = 68043$
 c $96217 - 8477 = 87740$
 d $70831 - 5925 = 64906$
 e $66314 - 8207 = 58107$
 f $75641 - 9073 = 66568$
 g $48502 - 6723 = 41779$
 h $55817 - 8204 = 47613$
 i $34251 - 6314 = 27937$
 j $75123 - 942 = 74181$
 k $85633 - 708 = 84925$
 l $968423 - 48621 = 919802$
 m $604238 - 76214 = 528024$
 n $306087 - 24321 = 281766$
 o $719625 - 8421 = 711204$
 p $962147 - 8467 = 953680$
 q $15219 - 5841 = 9378$
 r $762183 - 7610 = 754573$
 s $64283 - 5073 = 59210$

 t $672514 - 8447 = 664067$
 u $88452 - 9175 = 79277$
 v $69874 - 814 = 69060$
 w $793597 - 409 = 793188$
 x $556347 - 8200 = 548147$
 y $148264 - 38499 = 109765$
 z $268745 - 919 = 267826$

Refresher

1 a $18 - 6 = 12$ **b** $15 - 7 = 8$
 c $13 - 8 = 5$ **d** $9 - 4 = 5$
 e $11 - 5 = 6$ **f** $17 - 9 = 8$
 g $16 - 7 = 9$ **h** $15 - 11 = 4$
 i $19 - 15 = 4$ **j** $18 - 12 = 6$
 k $20 - 7 = 13$ **l** $14 - 9 = 5$
2 a $9523 - 821 = 8702$
 b $8172 - 3645 = 4527$
 c $9720 - 1813 = 7907$
 d $7389 - 5093 = 2296$
 e $9148 - 523 = 8625$
 f $5791 - 834 = 4957$
 g $6872 - 491 = 6381$
 h $57219 - 3705 = 53514$
 i $62977 - 4838 = 58139$
 j $74684 - 3971 = 70713$
 k $43972 - 5318 = 38654$
 l $39783 - 7825 = 31958$

Challenge

Answers will vary.

Week 9, Lesson 4 – Pages 82 and 83

Practice

1 a $62.48 - 14.8 = 47.68$
 b $157.8 - 84.57 = 73.23$
 c $2471.85 - 367.4 = 2104.45$
 d $982.67 - 31.962 = 950.708$
 e $7821.8 - 391.87 = 7429.93$
 f $507.68 - 89.791 = 417.889$
 g $4631.87 - 108.6 = 4523.27$
 h $42.591 - 7.31 = 35.281$
 i $6074.9 - 294.16 = 5780.74$
 j $75.91 - 8.63 = 67.28$
 k $143.84 - 51.726 = 92.114$
 l $18.421 - 9.47 = 8.951$
 m $7542.8 - 634.87 = 6907.93$

n 479.21 − 51.8 = 427.41
o 6372.8 − 483.69 = 5889.11
p 4805.1 − 698.83 = 4106.27
q 843.9 − 25.167 = 818.733
r 739.14 − 73.662 = 665.478
s 7114.5 − 43.81 = 7070.69
t 507.43 − 77.327 = 430.103
u 1068.6 − 106.49 = 962.11
v 29 736.74 − 452.8 = 29 283.94
w 891.542 − 38.4 = 853.142
x 7810.6 − 521.66 = 7288.94
y 652.94 − 48.61 = 604.33
z 6732.4 − 298.72 = 6433.68

Refresher

1 a 5.1 + 4.9 = 10   b 8.6 + 1.4 = 10
c 7.4 + 2.6 = 10   d 9.5 + 0.5 = 10
e 1.8 + 8.2 = 10   f 2.7 + 7.3 = 10
g 3.3 + 6.7 = 10   h 7.9 + 2.1 = 10
i 1.4 + 8.6 = 10   j 6.5 + 3.5 = 10
k 0.6 + 9.4 = 10   l 5.4 + 4.6 = 10
2 a 84.67 − 52.36 = 32.31
b 157.8 − 106.2 = 51.6
c 97.481 − 26.381 = 71.1
d 204.8 − 38.9 = 165.9
e 187.61 − 57.16 = 130.45
f 319.57 − 126.38 = 193.19
g 167.82 − 67.08 = 100.74
h 483.91 − 76.37 = 407.54
i 28.624 − 15.814 = 12.81
j 751.44 − 108.19 = 643.25
k 67.48 − 20.67 = 46.81
l 821.7 − 59.3 = 762.4
m 196.72 − 80.39 = 116.33
n 75.19 − 26.24 = 48.95
o 181.75 − 84.66 = 97.09

Challenge

1 a 426.75 − 219.58 = 207.17
    207.17 − 47.45 = 159.72
    159.72 − 131.3 = 28.42
b 84.279 − 32.842 = 51.437
    51.437 − 27.719 = 23.718
    23.718 − 14.614 = 9.104
c 1573.5 − 618.7 = 954.8
    954.8 − 450.1 = 504.7
    504.7 − 173.1 = 331.6

Week 9, Lesson 5 – Pages 84 and 85

Practice

1 a 62 + 37 = 99
    0.62 + 0.37 = 0.99
    6.2 + 3.7 = 9.9
    620 + 370 = 990
    6200 + 3700 = 9900
b 58 + 49 = 107
    0.58 + 0.49 = 1.07
    5.8 + 4.9 = 10.7
    580 + 490 = 1070
    5800 + 4900 = 10 700
c 86 + 35 = 121
    0.86 + 0.35 = 1.21
    8.6 + 3.5 = 12.1
    860 + 350 = 1210
    8600 + 3500 = 12 100
d 94 + 22 = 116
    0.94 + 0.22 = 1.16
    9.4 + 2.2 = 11.6
    940 + 220 = 1160
    9400 + 2200 = 11 600
2 a 76 + 84 = 160
    0.76 + 0.84 = 1.6
    7.6 + 8.4 = 16
    760 + 840 = 1600
    7600 + 8400 = 16 000
b 88 + 92 = 180
    0.88 + 0.92 = 1.8
    8.8 + 9.2 = 18
    880 + 920 = 1800
    8800 + 9200 = 18 000
c 27 + 80 = 107
    0.27 + 0.8 = 1.07
    2.7 + 8 = 10.7
    270 + 800 = 1070
    2700 + 8000 = 10 700
d 38 + 47 = 85
    0.38 + 0.47 = 0.85
    3.8 + 4.7 = 8.5
    380 + 470 = 850
    3800 + 4700 = 8500

Collins Primary Maths

e $59 + 28 = 87$
   $0.59 + 0.28 = 0.87$
   $5.9 + 2.8 = 8.7$
   $590 + 280 = 870$
   $5900 + 2800 = 8700$
f $63 + 43 = 106$
   $0.63 + 0.43 = 1.06$
   $6.3 + 4.3 = 10.6$
   $630 + 430 = 1060$
   $6300 + 4300 = 10\,600$
g $31 + 95 = 126$
   $0.31 + 0.95 = 1.26$
   $3.1 + 9.5 = 12.6$
   $310 + 950 = 1260$
   $3100 + 9500 = 12\,600$
h $57 + 92 = 149$
   $0.57 + 0.92 = 1.49$
   $5.7 + 9.2 = 14.9$
   $570 + 920 = 1490$
   $5700 + 9200 = 14\,900$
3 a $83 - 57 = 26$
   $0.83 - 0.57 = 0.26$
   $8.3 - 5.7 = 2.6$
   $830 - 570 = 260$
   $8300 - 5700 = 2600$
b $92 - 37 = 55$
   $0.92 - 0.37 = 0.55$
   $9.2 - 3.7 = 5.5$
   $920 - 370 = 550$
   $9200 - 3700 = 5500$
c $68 - 35 = 33$
   $0.68 - 0.35 = 0.33$
   $6.8 - 3.5 = 3.3$
   $680 - 350 = 330$
   $6800 - 3500 = 3300$
d $79 - 17 = 62$
   $0.79 - 0.17 = 0.62$
   $7.9 - 1.7 = 6.2$
   $790 - 170 = 620$
   $7900 - 1700 = 6200$
4 a $65 - 28 = 37$
   $0.65 - 0.28 = 0.37$
   $6.5 - 2.8 = 3.7$
   $650 - 280 = 370$
   $6500 - 2800 = 3700$

b $72 - 37 = 35$
   $0.72 - 0.37 = 0.35$
   $7.2 - 3.7 = 3.5$
   $720 - 370 = 350$
   $7200 - 3700 = 3500$
c $93 - 45 = 48$
   $0.93 - 0.45 = 0.48$
   $9.3 - 4.5 = 4.8$
   $930 - 450 = 480$
   $9300 - 4500 = 4800$
d $89 - 31 = 58$
   $0.89 - 0.31 = 0.58$
   $8.9 - 3.1 = 5.8$
   $890 - 310 = 580$
   $8900 - 3100 = 5800$
e $53 - 17 = 36$
   $0.53 - 0.17 = 0.36$
   $5.3 - 1.7 = 3.6$
   $530 - 170 = 360$
   $5300 - 1700 = 3600$
f $87 - 41 = 46$
   $0.87 - 0.41 = 0.46$
   $8.7 - 4.1 = 4.6$
   $870 - 410 = 460$
   $8700 - 4100 = 4600$
g $90 - 63 = 27$
   $0.90 - 0.63 = 0.27$
   $9 - 6.3 = 2.7$
   $900 - 630 = 270$
   $9000 - 6300 = 2700$
h $74 - 23 = 51$
   $0.74 - 0.23 = 0.51$
   $7.4 - 2.3 = 5.1$
   $740 - 230 = 510$
   $7400 - 2300 = 5100$

Refresher
1 a $0.04 + 0.06 = 0.1$
b $0.06 + 0.04 = 0.1$
c $0.01 + 0.09 = 0.1$
d $0.07 + 0.03 = 0.1$
e $0.09 + 0.01 = 0.1$
f $0.02 + 0.08 = 0.1$
g $0.05 + 0.05 = 0.1$
h $0.03 + 0.07 = 0.1$
i $0.08 + 0.02 = 0.1$

2 a $48 + 37 = 85$ **b** $41 + 28 = 69$
  c $37 + 68 = 105$ **d** $25 + 79 = 104$
  e $64 + 81 = 145$ **f** $97 - 51 = 46$
  g $84 - 67 = 17$ **h** $76 - 34 = 42$
  i $54 - 31 = 23$ **j** $57 - 29 = 28$
3 a $37 + 46 = 83$
     $370 + 460 = 830$
     $3700 + 4600 = 8300$
  b $19 + 25 = 44$
     $190 + 250 = 440$
     $1900 + 2500 = 4400$
  c $58 + 24 = 82$
     $580 + 240 = 820$
     $5800 + 2400 = 8200$
  d $68 + 17 = 85$
     $680 + 170 = 850$
     $6800 + 1700 = 8500$
  e $71 - 52 = 19$
     $710 - 520 = 190$
     $7100 - 5200 = 1900$
  f $85 - 38 = 47$
     $850 - 380 = 470$
     $8500 - 3800 = 4700$
  g $92 - 45 = 47$
     $920 - 450 = 470$
     $9200 - 4500 = 4700$

Challenge
Answers will vary

Week 10, Lesson 1 – Pages 86 and 87

Practice
1 a $5100 + 2300 = 7400$
  b $3300 + 4800 = 8100$
  c $6500 + 3000 = 9500$
  d $7200 + 1600 = 8800$
  e $4300 + 1900 = 6200$
  f $8400 + 6300 = 14700$
  g $7800 + 2600 = 10400$
  h $9300 + 2100 = 11400$
  i $7700 + 4500 = 12200$
  j $8300 + 4100 = 12400$
2 a $7500 - 2100 = 5400$
  b $8400 - 6300 = 2100$
  c $9700 - 2700 = 7000$

d $7600 - 1900 = 5700$
  e $3800 - 1300 = 2500$
  f $7600 - 4300 = 3300$
  g $9900 - 5100 = 4800$
  h $7500 - 3800 = 3700$
  i $9700 - 7100 = 2600$
3 a $7300 - 5100 = 2200$
  b $2400 + 5400 = 7800$
  c $9800 - 6300 = 3500$
  d $9000 - 3700 = 5300$
  e $3900 + 5900 = 9800$
  f $8400 - 6900 = 1500$
  g $6300 + 3300 = 9600$
  h $11\,000 - 2600 = 8400$
  i $8700 - 7500 = 1200$
  j $4000 + 8400 = 12\,400$
4 Answers will vary

Refresher
Answers will vary

Week 10, Lesson 2 – Pages 88 and 89

Practice
1 a $4.51 + 0.09 = 4.6$
  b $0.82 + 0.08 = 0.9$
  c $3.67 + 0.03 = 3.7$
  d $2.58 + 0.02 = 2.6$
  e $5.73 + 0.07 = 5.8$
  f $8.16 + 0.04 = 8.2$
  g $7.25 + 0.05 = 7.3$
  h $7.84 + 0.06 = 7.9$
  i $3.29 + 0.01 = 3.3$
  j $7.64 + 0.06 = 7.7$
  k $8.67 + 0.03 = 8.7$
  l $3.18 + 0.02 = 3.2$
2 a $4.82 + 0.18 = 5$ **b** $6.71 + 0.29 = 7$
  c $3.67 + 0.33 = 4$ **d** $0.91 + 0.09 = 1$
  e $2.54 + 0.46 = 3$ **f** $7.38 + 0.62 = 8$
  g $5.23 + 0.77 = 6$ **h** $6.15 + 0.85 = 7$
  i $9.48 + 0.52 = 10$ **j** $4.02 + 0.98 = 5$
  k $6.84 + 0.16 = 7$ **l** $3.11 + 0.89 = 4$
3 a $0.3 + 0.25 = 0.55$
  b $0.4 + 0.31 = 0.71$
  c $0.18 + 0.7 = 0.88$
  d $0.33 + 0.2 = 0.53$
  e $0.2 + 0.63 = 0.83$

Collins Primary Maths

f $0.4 + 0.59 = 0.99$
g $0.82 + 0.6 = 1.42$
h $0.73 + 0.7 = 1.43$
i $0.9 + 0.31 = 1.21$
j $0.74 + 0.8 = 1.54$
k $0.84 - 0.2 = 0.64$
l $0.5 - 0.31 = 0.19$
m $0.9 - 0.16 = 0.74$
n $0.24 - 0.1 = 0.14$
o $0.46 - 0.3 = 0.16$
p $0.68 - 0.5 = 0.18$
q $0.7 - 0.44 = 0.26$
r $0.8 - 0.11 = 0.69$
s $0.7 - 0.06 = 0.64$
t $0.67 - 0.2 = 0.47$

Refresher

1 a $48 + 52 = 100$ b $34 + 66 = 100$
  c $29 + 71 = 100$ d $17 + 83 = 100$
  e $35 + 65 = 100$ f $44 + 56 = 100$
  g $92 + 8 = 100$ h $52 + 48 = 100$
  i $73 + 27 = 100$ j $69 + 31 = 100$
  k $82 + 18 = 100$ l $95 + 5 = 100$
2 a $3.21 + 0.09 = 3.3$ b $4.52 + 0.08 = 4.6$
  $3.21 + 0.79 = 4$ $4.52 + 0.48 = 5$
  c $1.85 + 0.05 = 1.9$ d $2.34 + 0.06 = 2.4$
  $1.85 + 0.15 = 2$ $2.34 + 0.66 = 3$
  e $5.17 + 0.03 = 5.2$ f $3.19 + 0.01 = 3.2$
  $5.17 + 0.83 = 6$ $3.19 + 0.81 = 4$
  g $2.73 + 0.07 = 2.8$ h $5.46 + 0.04 = 5.5$
  $2.73 + 0.27 = 3$ $5.46 + 0.54 = 6$
  i $2.82 + 0.08 = 2.9$
  $2.82 + 0.18 = 3$
3 a $0.7 + 0.1 = 0.8$
  b $0.5 + 0.3 = 0.8$
  c $0.2 + 0.4 = 0.6$
  d $0.8 - 0.4 = 0.4$
  e $0.9 - 0.6 = 0.3$
  f $0.5 - 0.1 = 0.4$
  g $0.78 + 0.11 = 0.89$
  h $0.41 + 0.26 = 0.67$
  i $0.62 + 0.33 = 0.95$
  j $0.75 - 0.26 = 0.49$
  k $0.82 - 0.34 = 0.48$
  l $0.61 - 0.47 = 0.14$

Challenge

1 a $0.5 + 0.263 = 0.763$

b $0.15 + 631 = 0.781$
c $0.8 + 0.742 = 1.542$
d $0.2 + 0.759 = 0.959$
e $0.53 + 0.675 = 1.205$
f $0.896 - 0.32 = 0.576$
g $0.745 - 0.3 = 0.445$
h $0.886 - 0.1 = 0.786$
i $0.9 - 0.634 = 0.266$
j $0.78 - 0.351 = 0.429$
k $0.985 - 0.06 = 0.925$
l $0.72 + 0.168 = 0.888$

Week 10, Lesson 3 – Page 90 and 91

Practice

1 a $25 + 17 + 39 + 29 = 110$
  b $632 + 152 = 784$
  c $7965 + 2391 = 10\,356$
  d $635 + 198 = 833$
  e $8463 - 7963 = 500$
  f $960 - 352 = 608$
  g $14 + 25 + 36 + 98 = 173$
  h $78\,263 - 6354 = 71\,909$
  i $32 + 65 + 75 + 10 = 182$
  j $963 + 472 = 1435$
  k $36\,421 + 95\,200 = 131\,621$
  l $63 + 35 + 14 + 37 = 149$
  m $674 - 350 = 324$
  n $7514 - 3000 = 4514$
  o $6800 - 2600 = 4200$
  p $8400 + 6100 = 14\,500$
  q $84 + 69 = 153$
  r $6952 - 3841 = 3111$
  s $75\,320 + 52\,100 = 127\,420$
  t $9642 + 6300 = 15\,942$
  u $7500 - 2510 = 4990$
  v $82 + 63 + 41 + 37 = 223$
  w $63\,140 - 23\,400 = 39\,740$
  x $8692 + 3471 = 12\,163$
  y $7210 - 6321 = 889$

Refresher

1 a $31 + 25 + 51 = 107$
  b $74 + 38 + 20 = 132$
  c $61 + 53 + 87 = 201$
  d $55 + 39 + 48 = 142$

e 75 + 36 + 15 = 126
f 73 + 61 + 30 = 164
g 12 + 36 + 59 + 84 = 191
h 32 + 52 + 16 + 62 = 162
i 13 + 20 + 46 + 53 = 132
j 19 + 64 + 38 + 22 = 143
k 21 + 48 + 16 + 34 = 119
l 37 + 52 + 18 + 26 = 133

2 a 48 + 63 = 111   b 47 + 25 = 72
c 84 − 26 = 58   d 40 − 27 = 13
e 486 − 201 = 285   f 255 + 320 = 575
g 420 + 380 = 800   h 163 − 90 = 73
i 152 + 364 = 516   j 271 + 632 = 903
k 286 − 42 = 244   l 437 + 193 = 630

3 a 4885 + 3621 = 8506
b 8542 + 2704 = 11 246
c 7514 + 1397 = 8911
d 7852 + 5793 = 13 645
e 6985 + 3210 = 10 195
f 9862 − 3521 = 6341
g 5412 − 4213 = 1199
h 4125 − 3781 = 344
i 6914 − 3823 = 3091
j 9621 − 3541 = 6080
k 5861 − 4213 = 1648
l 7061 − 3469 = 3592

Challenge
1 a Correct
b Incorrect. Should be 4337
c Incorrect. Should be 294
d Correct
e Incorrect. Should be 38 724
f Incorrect. Should be 21 200
g Correct
h Correct
i Incorrect. Should be 18 375
j Incorrect. Should be + not −

~~~~~~~~~~~~~~

Week 10, Lesson 4 – Pages 92 and 93

Practice
1 a 180 pitta breads
b 120 packs, 720 pitta breads
c £18.90
2 a £25.75   b £6.30   c £146.70

3 a 4 coaches   b £288   c 624 people
4 a 980 matches per pack
b 100 boxes
c 98 000

Refresher
1 a 35 cups   b 8 cups
c 28 cups per week
2 a 23p   b £18.40   c 46p

Challenge
Open

~~~~~~~~~~~~~~

Week 10, Lesson 5 – Pages 94 and 95

Practice
1 a 9 hours   b 35 hours   c £502.65
2 a 540 airmail letters
b 90 letters
c 450 postcards
3 a 85p   b 20p   c £17
4 a 35p   b £3.50
c 5 bags of crisps

Refresher
1 a £3.96   b 10 roses   c £2.98
2 a £888   b £80
c 740 children came

Challenge
Sarah jumped 260 cm
Louise jumped 255 cm
Zoe jumped 265 cm
Rachel jumped 261 cm

~~~~~~~~~~~~~~

Week 11, Lesson 1 – Pages 96 and 97

Practice
1 a The product of 2 even numbers is even
b The product of 2 odd numbers is odd
c The product of 3 or more even numbers is even
d The product of 3 odd numbers is odd
e The product of 1 even and 1 odd number is even

Refresher
2 a, b, d, e, f, h, j, l, n, q, r, s, t
3 a 18 + 22 = 40

Collins Primary Maths

b $26 + 88 = 114$
c $45 + 33 = 78$
d $27 + 79 = 106$
e $12 + 14 + 16 = 42$
f $52 - 34 = 18$
g $89 - 47 = 42$
h $47 + 65 = 112$
i $15 + 27 + 39 = 81$
j $123 + 259 = 382$
k $86 + 92 = 178$
l $76 - 44 = 32$
m $97 - 63 = 34$
n $128 + 146 = 274$
o $77 + 114 = 191$
p $73 + 48 = 121$
q $243 - 137 = 106$
r $36 + 47 = 83$
s $181 - 97 = 84$
t $326 - 140 = 186$
u $152 - 36 = 116$
v $271 + 273 = 544$
w $235 + 262 = 497$
x $94 - 76 = 18$

Challenge

2 a, b, c, d, g, h, i, l, m, n, o, s, u
3 a $686 - 498 = 188$
 b $24 \times 15 = 360$
 c $3476 + 4598 = 8074$
 d $76 \times 8 = 608$
 e $8 \times 12 \times 14 = 1344$
 f $3257 - 1243 = 2014$
 g $7 \times 9 \times 11 = 693$
 h $6 \times 12 \times 24 = 1728$
 i $39 \times 17 = 663$
 j $638 + 422 + 374 = 1434$
 k $47 \times 51 = 2397$
 l $85 \times 25 = 2125$
 m $364 + 228 + 126 = 718$
 n $84 \times 19 = 1596$
 o $163 \times 7 = 1141$
 p $298 \times 8 = 2384$
 q $93 \times 27 = 2511$
 r $59 \times 42 = 2478$
 s $74 \times 36 = 2664$

 t $14 \times 8 \times 24 = 2688$
 u $13 \times 5 \times 9 = 585$

Week 11, Lesson 2 – Pages 98 and 99

Practice

1 a Common multiples are 12, 24, 36
 b Common multiples are 4, 8, 12, 16, 20
 c Common multiples are 30, 60
 d Common multiples are 9, 18, 27
 e Common multiples are 20, 40
 f Common multiples are 24, 48
 g Common multiple is 63
 h Common multiple is 56
2 60, 24, 30, 28, 36, 24

Refresher

1 $6 \times 9 = 54$	$6 \times 4 = 24$
$7 \times 9 = 63$	$4 \times 8 = 32$
$6 \times 6 = 36$	$9 \times 5 = 45$
$4 \times 14 = 56$	$9 \times 3 = 27$
$6 \times 7 = 42$	$6 \times 5 = 30$
$4 \times 7 = 28$	$9 \times 9 = 81$
$4 \times 4 = 16$	$8 \times 6 = 48$
$8 \times 9 = 72$	

Challenge

1 a Multiples of 8: 8, 16, 24, 32, 40, 48, 56, 64, 72, 80, 88, 96, 104, 112, 120, 128, 136, 144, ...
 Multiples of 15: 15, 30, 45, 60, 75, 90, 105, 120, 135, 150, 165, 180, 195, 210, 225, 240, ...
 b Common multiples: 120, 240, 360, 480
 c Lowest common multiple: 120
2 15
3 a 99, 198, 297, 396, 495
 b The units decrease by 1 each time while the hundreds increase by 1 each time
 c After 990, the units start again at 9 and the pattern is repeated: 594, 693, 792, 891, 990, 1089, 1188, 1287, ...
4 240 (after 60, 120, 180)
5 Every 72 seconds

Week 11, Lesson 3 – Pages 100 and 101

Practice

1 a 25, 50, 75, 100, 125, 150, 175, 200, 225, 250

  b (see c below)

  c Multiples of 25 always end in the digits 0 or 5.

2 A number is divisible by 25 if its last two digits are 00, 25, 50 or 75.

3 2050, 1625, 3475, 23 250, 9000, 47 125, 33 475, 6700

4 3.25, 5.00, 7.50, 3.75, 9.25

5 316, 2332, 492, 544, 1224, 708, 3428, 5652

6 472, 4256, 2088, 4264, 680, 2680

Refresher

1 a 1.25, 1.50, 1.75, 2.00, 2.25

  b 20, 24, 28, 32, 36

  c 40, 48, 56, 64, 72

  d 7.50, 7.75, 8.00, 8.25, 8.50

  e 9.25, 9.00, 8.75, 8.50, 8.25

  f −40, −32, −24, −16, −8

  g 0, −4, −8, −12, −16

  h 1.75, 1.50, 1.25, 1.00, 0.75

Challenge

1 a It could be true because a number is divisible by 25 if it ends in 00.

  b Yes, because the last 2 digits, 68, are divisible by 4.

  c 2000, 2004, 2008, 2012, 2016, 2020, 2024, 2028, 2032, 2036, 2040, 2044, 2048, 2052, 2056, 2060, 2064, 2068, 2072, 2076, 2080, 2088, 2092, 2096.

  d Yes, because a number is divisible by 8 if half its value is divisible by 4.

  e Yes, because the last 2 digits, 96, divide exactly by 4.

  f Yes, because the last 3 digits, 504, are divisible by 8.

Week 11, Lesson 4 – Pages 102 and 103

Practice

1 a Multiples of 2   b Multiples of 3

  c Multiples of 4   d Multiples of 8

  e Multiples of 9   f Multiples of 3

2 a 4323   b 2393   c 3074

  d 1388   e 2483

  f All the numbers belong in the box.

3 Refer to divisibility tests given in Pupil Book.

4 Answers will vary

Refresher

1 Answers will vary

Challenge

Answers will vary

Week 11, Lesson 5 – Pages 104 and 105

Practice

Number	Factors	N° factors
1	1	1
2	1, 2	2
3	1, 3	2
4	1, 2, 4	3
5	1, 5	2
6	1, 2, 3, 6	4
7	1, 7	2
8	1, 2, 4, 8	4
9	1, 3, 9	3
10	1, 2, 5, 10	4
11	1, 11	2
12	1, 2, 3, 4, 6, 12	6
13	1, 13	2
14	1, 2, 7, 14	4
15	1, 3, 5, 15	4
16	1, 2, 4, 8, 16	5
17	1, 17	2
18	1, 2, 3, 6, 9, 18	6
19	1, 19	2
20	1, 2, 4, 5, 10	5
21	1, 3, 7, 21	4
22	1, 2, 11, 22	4
23	1, 23	2

Collins Primary Maths

24	1, 2, 3, 4, 6, 8, 12, 24	8
25	1, 5, 25	3
26	1, 2, 13, 26	4
27	1, 3, 9, 27	4
28	1, 2, 4, 7, 14, 28	6
29	1, 29	2
30	1, 2, 3, 5, 6, 10, 15, 30	8
31	1, 31	2
32	1, 2, 4, 8, 16, 32	6
33	1, 3, 11, 33	4
34	1, 2, 17, 34	4
35	1, 5, 7, 35	4
36	1, 2, 3, 4, 6, 9, 12, 18, 36	9
37	1, 37	2
38	1, 2, 19, 38	4
39	1, 3, 13, 39	4
40	1, 2, 4, 5, 8, 10, 20, 40	8
41	1, 41	2
42	1, 2, 3, 6, 7, 14, 21, 42	8
43	1, 43	2
44	1, 2, 4, 11, 22, 44	6
45	1, 3, 5, 9, 15, 45	6
46	1, 2, 23, 46	4
47	1, 47	2
48	1, 2, 4, 6, 8, 12, 16, 24, 48	9
49	1, 7, 49	3
50	1, 2, 5, 10, 25, 50	6

2 2, 3, 5, 7, 11, 13, 17, 19, 23, 29, 31, 37, 41, 43, 47 Prime numbers

3 49, 25, 49 Odd square numbers

4 Square numbers

5 a 81
  b 64, 81

c Square numbers always have an odd number of factors. For odd square numbers, there are always only 3 factors.

Refresher

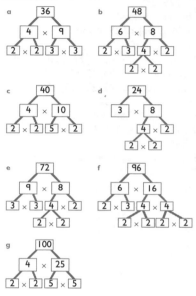

Challenge

1 Composite, because they have more than 2 factors.

2 Answers will vary

3 Yes. Other examples include 13, 19, 37.

4 a 502, 392, 1795, 462

  b These numbers are divisible either by 2 or 5. Prime numbers are divisible only by themselves or 1.

5 There are fewer prime numbers.

Answers

Week 1, Lesson 1 – Pages 4 and 5

Practice

1 a 5 821 800   **b** 4 310 556
  c 5 000 200 or 7 509 247
  d 2 123 431   **e** 9 452 549

2 seven million, five hundred and nine thousand, two hundred and forty-seven
nine million, six hundred and fifty-one thousand, nine hundred and seventy-seven
four million, three hundred and ten thousand, five hundred and fifty-six
five million, two hundred and ninety-nine thousand, seven hundred and thirty-eight
two million, one hundred and twenty-three thousand, four hundred and thirty-one
six million, six hundred and eighty-four thousand, nine hundred and thirty-seven
five million, eight hundred and twenty-one thousand, eight hundred
nine million, four hundred and fifty-two thousand, five hundred and forty-nine
five million, two hundred

3 a $496 \times 10 = 4960$
  b $2872 \times 100 = 287\,200$
  c $687 \div 10 = 68.7$
  d $3460 \div 100 = 34.6$
  e $96.7 \times 10 = 967$
  f $58\,703 \div 100 = 587.03$
  g $4872 \times 100 = 487\,200$
  h $586 \div 100 = 5.86$
  i $976 \times 10 = 9760$
  j $2870 \div 100 = 28.7$
  k $9700 \times 100 = 970\,000$
  l $62.8 \times 100 = 6280$
  m $27\,400 \div 100 = 274$
  n $68\,700 \div 10\,000 = 6.87$
  o $6 \div 100 = 0.06$
  p $5.2 \times 100 = 520$
  q $9731 \div 100 = 97.31$
  r $84 \div 100 = 0.84$
  s $8700 \times 10 = 87\,000$
  t $9\,300\,000 \div 10 = 930\,000$
  u $72\,863 \times 10 = 728\,630$
  v $56\,920 \div 100 = 569.2$
  w $572 \div 100 = 5.72$
  x $4.82 \times 100 = 482$
  y $0.3 \times 10 = 3$

Refresher

1 a 2000   **b** 200   **c** 90 000
  d 20   **e** 5   **f** 100 000
  g 40 000   **h** 6000   **i** 30 000

2 seven million, five hundred and twenty-six thousand, three hundred and ninety-five
eight million, six hundred and thirty-two thousand, one hundred and fifty

3 a $28 \times 10 = 280$
  b $45 \times 10 = 450$
  c $286 \times 100 = 28\,600$
  d $173 \times 10 = 1730$
  e $4862 \times 100 = 486\,200$
  f $7982 \times 10 = 79\,820$
  g $4.7 \times 10 = 47$
  h $3.12 \times 100 = 312$
  i $5.32 \times 10 = 53.2$
  j $9.67 \times 100 = 967$

4 a $9100 \div 10 = 910$
  b $7280 \div 10 = 728$
  c $1700 \div 100 = 17$
  d $300 \div 100 = 3$
  e $438\,000 \div 100 = 4380$
  f $58\,700 \div 10 = 5870$
  g $970 \div 100 = 9.7$
  h $45 \div 10 = 4.5$
  i $1273 \div 100 = 12.73$
  j $15.6 \div 10 = 1.56$

Collins Primary Maths

Challenge

a 100
b 128 000 pencils, 128 boxes
c 456 g

Week 1, Lesson 2 – Pages 6 and 7

Practice

1		10	100	1000
	a	452 390	452 400	452 000
	b	171 360	171 400	171 000
	c	649 230	649 200	649 000
	d	100 510	100 500	101 000
	e	643 850	643 800	644 000
	f	7 638 200	7 638 200	7 638 000
	g	8 632 480	8 632 500	8 632 000
	h	9 158 220	9 158 200	9 158 000
	i	2 633 500	2 633 500	2 634 000
	j	6 348 220	6 348 200	6 348 000

2 a 1000, 4000, 9000 b 500, 6000, 7000
  c 2000, 5000, 9500 d $-45, -25, -2$
  e $-40, -20, -5$ f $-90, -50, -10$
  g $-95, -65, -15$ h $-160, -110, -25$
  i 0.01, 0.05, 0.09 j 0.02, 0.06, 0.08

Refresher

1 a 650, 700   b 820, 800
  c 480, 500   d 550, 600
  e 370, 400   f 3610, 3600
  g 4550, 4600   h 7930, 7900
  i 76 820, 76 800 j 91 360, 91 400
2 a 300, 500, 900   b 100, 200, 800
  c 1000, 2500, 4000 d 500, 2000, 4500
  e $-9, -5, -1$ f $-8, -6, -2$
  g 0.4, 0.5, 0.9   h 0.1, 0.6, 0.8

Challenge

1 a 350, 500, 850
  b 0.061, 0.066, 0.068
  c 1.764, 1.765, 1.769
  d 2.511, 2.516, 2.518
2 Answers will vary

Week 1, Lesson 3 – Pages 8 and 9

Practice

1 a $\frac{1}{4}$ b $\frac{1}{8}$ c $\frac{1}{3}$ d $\frac{1}{6}$
2 a $\frac{1}{6}$ b $\frac{6}{7}$ c $\frac{1}{2}$ d $\frac{2}{3}$
3 Answers will vary, but accept answers similar to those below.

a $\frac{2}{10}$
b $\frac{3}{8}$
c $\frac{3}{5}$
d $\frac{7}{15}$

4 Answers will vary
5 Answers will vary
6 Answers will vary
7 Answers will vary
8 Answers will vary

Refresher

1 a $-78, -10, -6, 0, 2, 63$
  b $-52, -25, -5, 2, 5, 25$
  c $-100, -58, -7, 49, 59, 105$
  d $-101, -48, -23, 12, 72, 85$
  e $-72, -51, -7, -1, 73, 86, 100$
2 Answers will vary
3 Answers will vary
4 Answers will vary
5 Answers will vary

Challenge

Answers will vary

Week 2, Lesson 1 – Pages 10 and 11

Practice

a 93 pupils can attend (round down)
b 86 rows needed (round down)
c 33 boxes needed (round up)
d 78 brochures sold
e 96 rows can be filled (round down)
f 95 packs can be made up (round down)

Refresher

1 4: 26 → 24
      49 → 48
      62 → 60
      83 → 80
      101 → 100
      163 → 160
    9: 65 → 63
      89 → 81
      58 → 54
      186 → 180
      273 → 270
      364 → 360
2 6: 39 → 42
      115 → 120
      70 → 72
      175 → 180
      598 → 600
      357 → 360
    5: 52 → 55
      121 → 125
      326 → 330
      419 → 420
      272 → 275
      463 → 465
    8: 43 → 48
      62 → 64
      79 → 80
      94 → 96
      86 → 88
      158 → 160

Challenge

Answers will vary

Week 2, Lesson 2 – Pages 12 and 13

Practice

1 a £26.30	b £3.12	c £192
d £18.90	e £27.50	f £149
g £3.51	h £2.45	i £5.12
j £56.80	k £414	l £599
m £0.72	n £7.02	o £1.70
p £0.74		

2 a £0.75   b £0.60   c £5.20   d £0.68

Refresher

Tin soup: $4 \times £0.52 = £2.08$
Champagne: $3 \times £24 = £72$
Bread: $9 \times £0.46 = £4.14$
Bottle drink: $10 \times £1.52 = £15.20$
Mini B-B-Q: $3 \times £53 = £159$
Margarine: $5 \times £0.65 = £3.25$
Spaghetti: $6 \times £0.49 = £2.94$
Tin tomatoes: $100 \times £0.09 = £9$
Milk: $2 \times £0.36 = £0.72$
Washing powder: $10 \times £4.82 = 48.20$

Challenge

Child 1: 10.80
Child 2: 3.24
Child 3: 83.2
Child 3 had the highest score.

Week 2, Lesson 3 – Pages 14 and 15

Practice

1 Answers will vary. Model answers:
   a $250 \times 12 = 3000$
   b $350 \times 20 = 7000$
   c $450 \times 25 = 11\,250$
   d $470 \times 12 = 5640$
   e $240 \times 30 = 7200$
   f $368 \times 50 = 18\,400$
   g $260 \times 40 = 10\,400$
   h $176 \times 40 = 7040$
   i $220 \times 60 = 13\,200$
   j $842 \times 20 = 16\,840$
   k $190 \times 90 = 17\,100$
   l $620 \times 30 = 18\,600$

2 a $254 \times 13 = 3302$

×	200	50	4	
10	2000	500	40	2540
3	600	150	12	+ 762
				3302

b $342 \times 23 = 7866$
c $457 \times 25 = 11\,425$
d $467 \times 14 = 6538$
e $236 \times 28 = 6608$

Collins Primary Maths

f $368 \times 47 = 17\,296$
g $263 \times 35 = 9205$
h $176 \times 38 = 6688$
i $219 \times 64 = 14\,016$
j $842 \times 19 = 15\,998$
k $194 \times 86 = 16\,684$
l $624 \times 27 = 16\,848$

Refresher

1 a $274 \rightarrow 200 + 70 + 4$
 b $368 \rightarrow 300 + 60 + 8$
 c $412 \rightarrow 400 + 10 + 2$
 d $657 \rightarrow 600 + 50 + 7$
 e $810 \rightarrow 800 + 10$
 f $403 \rightarrow 400 + 3$
 g $629 \rightarrow 600 + 20 + 9$
 h $532 \rightarrow 500 + 30 + 2$
 i $195 \rightarrow 100 + 90 + 5$
 j $711 \rightarrow 700 + 10 + 1$
 k $205 \rightarrow 200 + 5$
 l $350 \rightarrow 300 + 50$
2 a $452 \rightarrow 450, 500$
 b $638 \rightarrow 640, 600$
 c $327 \rightarrow 330, 300$
 d $424 \rightarrow 420, 400$
 e $710 \rightarrow 710, 700$
 f $569 \rightarrow 570, 600$
 g $271 \rightarrow 270, 300$
 h $183 \rightarrow 180, 200$
 i $606 \rightarrow 610, 600$
 j $595 \rightarrow 600, 600$

Challenge

a $227 \times 25 = 5675$

$\times$	200	20	7	
20	4000	400	140	4540
5	1000	100	35	+ 1135
				5675

b $326 \times 14 = 4564$
c $438 \times 22 = 9636$
d $591 \times 25 = 14\,775$
e $374 \times 24 = 8976$
f $169 \times 33 = 5577$
g $125 \times 48 = 6000$
h $462 \times 15 = 6930$
i $634 \times 34 = 21\,556$
j $716 \times 19 = 13\,604$

Week 2, Lesson 4 – Pages 16 and 17

Practice

1 a $30 \times 9 = 270$ b $100 \times 7 = 700$
 $600 \times 9 = 5400$ $200 \times 7 = 1400$
 $40 \times 9 = 360$ $50 \times 7 = 350$
 $200 \times 9 = 1800$ $400 \times 7 = 2800$
 $900 \times 9 = 8100$ $800 \times 7 = 5600$
 $700 \times 9 = 6300$ $60 \times 7 = 420$
 c $600 \times 8 = 4800$
 $300 \times 8 = 2400$
 $50 \times 8 = 400$
 $400 \times 8 = 3200$
 $70 \times 8 = 560$
 $90 \times 8 = 720$

2 a $227 \times 33 \approx 230 \times 30 = 6900$

						2	2	7
				$\times$			3	3
(2	0	0	$\times$	3	3)	6	6	0	0
	(2	0	$\times$	3	3)		6	6	0
		(7	$\times$	3	3)		2	3	1
						7	4	9	1

b $342 \times 17 \approx 350 \times 15 = 5250$
 $342 \times 17 = 5814$
c $189 \times 24 \approx 200 \times 25 = 5000$
 $189 \times 24 = 4536$
d $152 \times 34 \approx 150 \times 35 = 5250$
 $152 \times 34 = 5168$
e $137 \times 52 \approx 140 \times 50 = 7000$
 $137 \times 52 = 7124$
f $264 \times 25 \approx 260 \times 25 = 6500$
 $264 \times 25 = 6600$
g $284 \times 28 \approx 280 \times 30 = 8400$
 $284 \times 28 = 7952$
h $326 \times 29 \approx 330 \times 30 = 9900$
 $326 \times 29 = 9454$
i $438 \times 47 \approx 440 \times 50 = 22\,000$
 $438 \times 47 = 20\,586$
j $678 \times 49 \approx 680 \times 50 = 34\,000$
 $678 \times 49 = 33\,222$

Refresher

a $176 \times 13 \approx 180 \times 12 = 2160$

$\times$	100	70	6	
10	1000	700	60	1760
3	300	210	18	+ 528
				$\underline{2288}$
				$_1$

b $149 \times 25 \approx 150 \times 25 = 3750$
$149 \times 25 = 3725$

c $234 \times 32 \approx 250 \times 30 = 7500$
$234 \times 32 = 7488$

d $194 \times 37 \approx 190 \times 40 = 7600$
$194 \times 37 = 7178$

e $245 \times 14 \approx 250 \times 15 = 3750$
$245 \times 14 = 3430$

f $376 \times 12 \approx 380 \times 12 = 4560$
$376 \times 12 = 4512$

g $246 \times 28 \approx 246 \times 30 = 7380$
$246 \times 28 = 6888$

h $319 \times 45 \approx 300 \times 45 = 13\,500$
$319 \times 45 = 14\,355$

i $462 \times 38 \approx 450 \times 40 = 18\,000$
$462 \times 38 = 17\,556$

Challenge

1 $346 \times 25 = 8650$
2 $537 \times 19 = 10\,203$

Week 2, Lesson 5 – Pages 18 and 19

Practice

1 a $157 \times 26 \approx 160 \times 25 = 4000$
b $234 \times 14 \approx 250 \times 15 = 3750$
c $175 \times 29 \approx 175 \times 30 = 5250$
d $268 \times 13 \approx 270 \times 15 = 4050$
e $278 \times 22 \approx 280 \times 20 = 5600$
f $356 \times 25 \approx 350 \times 25 = 8750$
g $384 \times 29 \approx 380 \times 30 = 11\,400$
h $293 \times 72 \approx 300 \times 70 = 21\,000$
i $395 \times 36 \approx 400 \times 35 = 14\,000$
j $476 \times 27 \approx 480 \times 25 = 12\,000$
k $458 \times 39 \approx 450 \times 40 = 18\,000$
l $584 \times 37 \approx 580 \times 40 = 23\,200$

2 a $157 \times 26 \approx 160 \times 25 = 4000$

						1	5	7
				$\times$			2	6
(1	0	0	$\times$	2	6)	2	6	0	0
	(5	0	$\times$	2	6)	1	3	0	0
		(7	$\times$	2	6)		1	8	2
						4	0	8	2

b $234 \times 14 = 3276$
c $175 \times 29 = 5075$
d $268 \times 13 = 3484$
e $278 \times 22 = 6116$
f $356 \times 25 = 8900$
g $384 \times 29 = 11\,136$
h $293 \times 72 = 21\,096$
i $395 \times 36 = 14\,220$
j $476 \times 27 = 12\,852$
k $458 \times 39 = 17\,862$
l $584 \times 37 = 21\,608$

Refresher

1 a $156 \times 37 \rightarrow 100 \times 37 = 3700$
$ 50 \times 37 = 1850$
$ 6 \times 37 = \underline{222}$
$ 5772$

or $156 \times 37 \rightarrow 156 \times 30 = 4680$
$ 156 \times 7 = \underline{1092}$
$ 5772$

b $228 \times 15 = 3420$
c $345 \times 24 = 8280$
d $196 \times 33 = 6468$
e $429 \times 26 = 11\,154$
f $484 \times 63 = 30\,492$
g $748 \times 53 = 39\,644$
h $927 \times 86 = 79\,722$

Challenge

Answers will vary

Collins Primary Maths

Week 3, Lesson 1 – Pages 20 and 21

Practice

1 Answers will vary. Model answers:
- **a** $420 \div 20 = 21$
- **b** $640 \div 20 = 32$
- **c** $540 \div 10 = 54$
- **d** $670 \div 10 = 67$
- **e** $500 \div 25 = 20$
- **f** $760 \div 20 = 38$
- **g** $930 \div 30 = 31$
- **h** $900 \div 30 = 30$
- **i** $1000 \div 25 = 40$
- **j** $800 \div 10 = 80$
- **k** $850 \div 25 = 34$
- **l** $390 \div 15 = 26$

2a $455 \div 13 \approx 450 \div 15 = 30$

$$
\begin{array}{r}
13\overline{)455} \\
-\ 260\ (20 \times 13) \\
\hline
195 \\
-\ 130\ (10 \times 13) \\
\hline
65 \\
-\ 65\ (5 \times 13) \\
\hline
0
\end{array}
$$

Answer = 35
- **b** $624 \div 16 = 39$
- **c** $946 \div 22 = 43$
- **d** $672 \div 24 = 28$
- **e** $480 \div 15 = 32$
- **f** $816 \div 12 = 68$
- **g** $806 \div 26 = 31$
- **h** $896 \div 32 = 28$
- **i** $459 \div 17 = 27$
- **j** $893 \div 19 = 47$
- **k** $966 \div 23 = 42$
- **l** $936 \div 18 = 52$
- **m** $546 \div 21 = 26$
- **n** $882 \div 14 = 63$

3 £23 each

4 43 books on each shelf

Refresher

1
- **a** $12 \rightarrow 12 \times 2 = 24$
- **b** $59 \rightarrow 59 \times 2 = 118$
- **c** $86 \rightarrow 86 \times 2 = 172$
- **d** $91 \rightarrow 91 \times 2 = 182$
- **e** $24 \rightarrow 24 \times 2 = 48$
- **f** $79 \rightarrow 79 \times 2 = 158$
- **g** $67 \rightarrow 67 \times 2 = 134$
- **h** $53 \rightarrow 53 \times 2 = 106$
- **i** $48 \rightarrow 48 \times 2 = 96$
- **j** $34 \rightarrow 34 \times 2 = 68$
- **k** $47 \rightarrow 47 \times 2 = 94$
- **l** $15 \rightarrow 15 \times 2 = 30$

2a $18 \times 10 = 180$
- **b** $16 \times 10 = 160$
- **c** $57 \times 10 = 570$
- **d** $25 \times 10 = 250$
- **e** $68 \times 10 = 680$
- **f** $72 \times 10 = 720$
- **g** $28 \times 10 = 280$
- **h** $74 \times 10 = 740$
- **i** $33 \times 10 = 330$
- **j** $49 \times 10 = 490$
- **k** $65 \times 10 = 650$
- **l** $80 \times 10 = 800$

Challenge

$346 \div 12 = 28 \ \text{r}10 = 28\frac{5}{6}$

$839 \div 24 = 34 \ \text{r}23 = 34\frac{23}{24}$

$657 \div 29 = 22 \ \text{r}19 = 22\frac{19}{29}$

Week 3, Lesson 2 – Pages 22 and 23

Practice

1a $754 \div 13 \approx 750 \div 15 = 50$

$$
\begin{array}{r}
13\overline{)754} \\
-\ 650\ (50 \times 13) \\
\hline
104 \\
-\ 104\ (8 \times 13) \\
\hline
0
\end{array}
$$

Answer = 58
- **b** $930 \div 15 = 62$
- **c** $912 \div 24 = 38$
- **d** $884 \div 26 = 34$
- **e** $882 \div 18 = 49$
- **f** $969 \div 17 = 57$
- **g** $957 \div 29 = 33$
- **h** $992 \div 32 = 31$
- **i** $952 \div 34 = 28$
- **j** $989 \div 43 = 23$
- **k** $864 \div 54 = 16$
- **l** $900 \div 25 = 36$
- **m** $768 \div 48 = 16$
- **n** $924 \div 33 = 28$

2a 56 boxes in a carton
- **b** £39 per night
- **c** Each person receives £42.
- **d** The car uses 63 l of petrol on average per day.

Refresher

1
- **a** $150 \div 15 = 10$
- **b** $270 \div 27 = 10$
- **c** $320 \div 32 = 10$
- **d** $120 \div 12 = 10$
- **e** $240 \div 24 = 10$
- **f** $350 \div 35 = 10$

2
- **a** $300 \div 15 = 20$
- **b** $240 \div 12 = 20$
- **c** $360 \div 18 = 20$
- **d** $400 \div 20 = 20$
- **e** $280 \div 14 = 20$
- **f** $460 \div 23 = 20$

3
- **a** $450 \div 15 = 30$
- **b** $750 \div 25 = 30$
- **c** $480 \div 12 = 40$
- **d** $390 \div 13 = 30$
- **e** $440 \div 11 = 40$
- **f** $690 \div 23 = 30$

4a $770 \div 11 = 70$ **b** $640 \div 32 = 20$
  c $600 \div 12 = 50$ **d** $540 \div 60 = 9$
  e $450 \div 50 = 9$

Challenge
a $870 \div 24 = 36\frac{1}{4}$
b $825 \div 12 = 68\frac{3}{4}$
c $1365 \div 25 = 54\frac{3}{5}$
d $1032 \div 16 = 64\frac{1}{2}$
e $1320 \div 36 = 36\frac{2}{3}$
f $1662 \div 42 = 39\frac{4}{7}$
g $879 \div 18 = 48\frac{5}{6}$
h $1720 \div 48 = 35\frac{5}{6}$
i $2110 \div 40 = 52\frac{3}{4}$

Week 3, Lesson 3 – Pages 24 and 25

Practice

1 a $768 \div 16 \approx 750 \div 15 = 50$

```
    16)768
      −480  (30 × 16)
       288
      −160  (10 × 16)
       128
      −128  (8 × 16)
         0
```
  Answer $= 48$

or
```
        48
    16)768
      −64
      128
     −128
        0
```

b $621 \div 23 = 27$ **c** $992 \div 32 = 31$
d $931 \div 19 = 49$ **e** $850 \div 25 = 34$
f $984 \div 41 = 24$ **g** $784 \div 14 = 56$
h $816 \div 24 = 34$ **i** $891 \div 27 = 33$
j $972 \div 18 = 54$ **k** $828 \div 36 = 23$
l $841 \div 29 = 29$
2 Answers will vary

Refresher
a 16, 32, 48, 64, 80
b 25, 50, 75, 100, 125
c 14, 28, 42, 56, 70
d 9, 18, 27, 36, 45
e 22, 44, 66, 88, 110
f 31, 62, 93, 124, 155
g 40, 80, 120, 160, 200
h 52, 104, 156, 208, 260
i 70, 140, 210, 280, 350
j 15, 30, 45, 60, 75
k 90, 180, 270, 360, 450
l 33, 66, 99, 132, 165
m 24, 48, 72, 96, 120
n 50, 100, 150, 200, 250
o 13, 26, 39, 52, 65
p 42, 84, 126, 168, 210
q 80, 160, 240, 320, 400
r 35, 70, 105, 140, 175
s 61, 122, 183, 244, 305
t 65, 130, 195, 260, 325

Challenge
1 $1127 \div 23 = 49$ **2** $304 \div 16 = 19$
  $882 \div 18 = 49$ $944 \div 16 = 59$
  $588 \div 12 = 49$ $1344 \div 16 = 84$
  $1225 \div 25 = 49$ $720 \div 16 = 45$
  $1764 \div 36 = 49$ $1008 \div 16 = 63$

Week 3, Lesson 4 – Pages 26 and 27

Practice
1 £7150
2 £6600, £660
3 £3900
4 £46.40, £232
5 £1820, £2860
6 £195, £146.25
7 £2548
8 £46

Refresher
1 a $66 \div 8 = 8\frac{1}{4}$
  b $75 \div 9 = 8\frac{1}{3}$
  c $124 \div 6 = 20\frac{2}{3}$
  d $95 \div 9 = 10\frac{5}{9}$
  e $181 \div 3 = 60\frac{1}{3}$
  f $216 \div 7 = 30\frac{6}{7}$
  g $242 \div 8 = 30\frac{1}{4}$
  h $105 \div 10 = 10\frac{1}{2}$
  i $56 \div 6 = 9\frac{1}{3}$
  j $83 \div 4 = 20\frac{3}{4}$

Collins Primary Maths

k $252 \div 10 = 25\frac{1}{5}$

l $162 \div 4 = 40\frac{1}{2}$

m $93 \div 5 = 18\frac{3}{5}$

n $366 \div 9 = 40\frac{2}{3}$

2 a $£1 \div 5 = 25p$

b $£5 \div 10 = 50p$

c $£3 \div 3 = £1$

d $£8 \div 5 = £1.60$

e $£60 \div 12 = £5$

f $£80 \div 20 = £4$

g $£9 \div 5 = £1.80$

h $£2 \div 5 = 40p$

i $£5 \div 4 = £1.25$

j $£4 \div 5 = 80p$

k $£7 \div 2 = £3.50$

l $£55 \div 11 = £5$

m $£101 \div 20 = £5.05$

n $£10 \div 4 = £2.50$

Challenge

1 a £10 660 per year

b £16 380 per year

c £16 848 per year

2 a £888.33 per month

b £1365 per month

c £1404 per month

3 a or b

Week 3 Lesson 5 – Pages 28 and 29

Practice

1 a Computer: £998.75
Printer: £305.50
Lap top: £1198.50
Camera: £446.50
Mobile phone: £47

b £1043.40

c Before VAT: £2550
After VAT: £2996.25

d £70.50

e Peak: 50 min
Off-peak: 100 min

f New price: £918
Inc VAT: £1078.65

Refresher

a £5950

b £12 240

c £21 280

d £102 000

e Computer: £680, lap top: £816

f Printer: £221, camera: £323, mobile phone: £34

Challenge

1 £5992.50

2 £7490.63, £624.22 per month

Week 4, Lesson 1 – Pages 30 and 31

Practice

1 a $\frac{5}{8} = \frac{10}{16}, \frac{10}{16}, \frac{3}{4} = \frac{12}{16}$

b $1\frac{5}{21}, 1\frac{6}{21}, 1\frac{7}{21}$ ($1\frac{5}{21}, 1\frac{2}{7}, 1\frac{1}{3}$)

c $2\frac{12}{18}, 2\frac{14}{18}, 2\frac{15}{18}$ ($2\frac{2}{3}, 2\frac{7}{9}, 2\frac{5}{6}$)

d $5\frac{3}{12}, 5\frac{4}{12}$ and $5\frac{4}{12}$ ($5\frac{1}{4}, 5\frac{4}{12}$ and $5\frac{1}{3}$)

e $6\frac{12}{20}, 6\frac{14}{20}, 6\frac{16}{20}$ ($6\frac{3}{5}, 6\frac{7}{10}, 6\frac{16}{20}$)

f $2\frac{7}{14}, 2\frac{11}{14}, 2\frac{12}{14}$ ($2\frac{1}{2}, 2\frac{11}{14}, 2\frac{6}{7}$)

g $4\frac{30}{50}, 4\frac{36}{50}, 4\frac{45}{50}$ ($4\frac{3}{5}, 4\frac{18}{25}, 4\frac{9}{10}$)

h $7\frac{55}{100}, 7\frac{73}{100}, 7\frac{80}{100}$ ($7\frac{11}{20}, 7\frac{73}{100}, 7\frac{8}{10}$)

i $9\frac{8}{32}, 9\frac{9}{32}, 9\frac{16}{32}$ ($9\frac{2}{8}, 9\frac{9}{32}, 9\frac{1}{2}$)

j $12\frac{6}{30}, 12\frac{20}{30}, 12\frac{23}{30}$ ($12\frac{1}{5}, 12\frac{4}{6}, 12\frac{23}{30}$)

2 a $3\frac{1}{4} = 3\frac{2}{8}$ and $3\frac{1}{2} = 3\frac{4}{8}$: halfway $= 3\frac{3}{8}$

b $5\frac{1}{3} = 5\frac{2}{6}$ and $5\frac{2}{3} = 5\frac{4}{6}$: halfway $= 5\frac{3}{6}$

c $3\frac{2}{5} = 3\frac{4}{10}$ and $3\frac{3}{5} = 3\frac{6}{10}$: halfway $= 3\frac{5}{10}$

d $1\frac{4}{5} = 1\frac{24}{30}$ and $1\frac{2}{3} = 1\frac{20}{30}$: halfway $= 1\frac{22}{30}$

e $6\frac{8}{10}$ and $6\frac{2}{5} = 6\frac{4}{10}$: halfway $= 6\frac{6}{10}$

f $9\frac{6}{12}$ and $9\frac{2}{3} = 9\frac{8}{12}$: halfway $= 9\frac{7}{12}$

g $4\frac{2}{8} = 4\frac{4}{16}$ and $4\frac{6}{16}$: halfway $= 4\frac{5}{16}$

h $8\frac{6}{10} = 8\frac{12}{20}$ and $8\frac{4}{5}$: halfway $= 8\frac{8}{20}$

i $1\frac{4}{9}$ and $1\frac{2}{3} = 1\frac{6}{9}$: halfway $= 1\frac{5}{9}$

j $2\frac{3}{5} = 2\frac{9}{15}$ and $2\frac{1}{3} = 2\frac{5}{15}$: halfway $= 2\frac{7}{15}$

Refresher

1 a $\frac{2}{8}, \frac{3}{8}, \frac{4}{8}$

b $\frac{16}{24}, \frac{18}{24}, \frac{21}{24}$

c $\frac{2}{6}, \frac{3}{6}, \frac{4}{6}$

d $\frac{2}{8}, \frac{4}{8}, \frac{5}{8}$

e $\frac{8}{20}, \frac{12}{20}, \frac{15}{20}$

f $\frac{3}{12}, \frac{7}{12}, \frac{8}{12}$

g $\frac{12}{20}, \frac{14}{20}, \frac{16}{20}$

h $\frac{4}{12}, \frac{8}{12}, \frac{9}{12}$

i $\frac{12}{18}, \frac{14}{18}, \frac{14}{18}$

j $\frac{6}{12}, \frac{9}{12}, \frac{10}{12}$

k $\frac{3}{15}, \frac{10}{15}, \frac{11}{15}$

l $\frac{7}{30}, \frac{10}{30}, \frac{18}{30}$

Challenge

Open

Week 4, Lesson 2 – Pages 32 and 33

Practice

1 a 0.375 **b** 0.556 **c** 0.462 **d** 0.8
 e 0.167 **f** 0.76 **g** 0.667 **h** 0.833
 i 0.15 **j** 0.467 **k** 0.188 **l** 0.357

2 a $\frac{76}{100} = \frac{19}{25}$ **b** $\frac{586}{1000} = \frac{293}{500}$ **c** $\frac{6}{100} = \frac{3}{50}$
 d $\frac{92}{100} = \frac{23}{25}$ **e** $\frac{265}{1000} = \frac{53}{200}$ **f** $\frac{108}{1000} = \frac{27}{250}$
 g $\frac{94}{100} = \frac{47}{50}$ **h** $\frac{12}{100} = \frac{3}{25}$ **i** $\frac{689}{1000}$

Refresher

1 a $\frac{1}{2} = 0.5$ **b** $\frac{1}{4} = 0.25$ **c** $\frac{3}{4} = 0.75$
 d $\frac{1}{5} = 0.2$ **e** $\frac{1}{10} = 0.1$

2 a 0.6 **b** 0.125 **c** 0.7 **d** 0.45
 e 0.72 **f** 0.75 **g** 0.4 **h** 0.3
 i 0.28

Challenge

a $58\% = \frac{29}{50} = 0.58$ **b** $19\% = \frac{19}{100} = 0.19$
c $39\% = \frac{39}{100} = 0.39$ **d** $48\% = \frac{12}{25} = 0.48$
e $22\% = \frac{11}{50} = 0.22$ **f** $64\% = \frac{16}{25} = 0.64$
g $81\% = \frac{81}{100} = 0.81$ **h** $65\% = \frac{13}{20} = 0.65$
i $45\% = \frac{9}{20} = 0.45$ **j** $72\% = \frac{18}{25} = 0.72$

Week 4, Lesson 3 – Pages 34 and 35

Practice

1 a 0.27, 0.4, 0.57 **b** 0.4, 0.44, 0.58
 c 0.67, 0.72, 0.8 **d** 0.14, 0.35, 0.38
 e 0.375, 0.53, 0.55 **f** 0.4, 0.54, 0.86
 g 0.4, 0.44, 0.63 **h** 0.784, 0.8, 0.96
 i 0.286, 0.375, 0.382
 j 0.5, 0.625, 0.67 **k** 0.53, 0.54, 0.67
 l 0.22, 0.375, 0.57 **m** 0.18, 0.24, 0.25
 n 0.11, 0.12, 0.125 **o** 0.30, 0.56, 0.83
 p 0.75, 0.846, 0.857 **q** 0.11, 0.176, 0.182
 r 0.28, 0.67, 0.69 **s** 0.083, 0.71, 0.875
 t 0.27, 0.33, 0.35 **u** 0.8, 0.83, 0.86

Refresher

 a 0.66, 0.8 **b** 0.25, 0.375
 c 0.9, 0.96 **d** 0.625, 0.84
 e 0.17, 0.25 **f** 0.33, 0.35
 g 0.6, 0.68 **h** 0.75, 0.8
 i 0.1, 0.12 **j** 0.8, 0.875
 k 0.32, 0.4 **l** 0.3, 0.37

Challenge

a
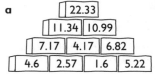

b

Week 4, Lesson 4 – Pages 36 and 37

Practice

1 a 3.02, 3.102, 3.2, 3.254, 3.26, 3.367
 b 5.2, 5.59, 5.9, 5.903, 5.921, 5.95
 c 7.004, 7.04, 7.4, 7.406, 7.41, 7.426
 d 8.1, 8.103, 8.11, 8.183, 8.8, 8.83
 e 1.55, 1.57, 1.577, 1.7, 1.75, 1.755
 f 2.1, 2.14, 2.8, 2.841, 2.88, 2.889
 g 9.006, 9.06, 9.6, 9.66, 9.669, 9.69
 h 0.004, 0.04, 0.4, 0.402, 0.456, 0.56
 i 0.2, 0.22, 0.225, 0.226, 0.26, 0.62
 j 1.8, 1.808, 1.88, 1.888, 1.899, 1.98

2 a 12.601, 12.602, 12.603, 12.604, 12.605, 12.606, 12.607, 12.608, 12.609
 b 30.541, 30.542, 30.543, 30.544, 30.545, 30.546, 30.547
 c 24.601, 24.602, 24.603, 24.604, 24.605, 24.606, 24.607, 24.608
 d 72.991, 72.992, 72.993, 72.994, 72.995, 72.996, 72.997, 72.998, 72.999, 73.000
 e 15.471, 15.472, 15.473, 15.474, 15.475, 15.476, 15.477, 15.478
 f 62.02, 62.03, 62.04, 62.05, 62.06, 62.07, 62.08, 62.09
 g 54.811, 54.812, 54.813, 54.814, 54.815, 54.816
 h 38.422, 38.423, 38.424, 38.425, 38.426, 38.427, 38.428, 38.429

Collins Primary Maths

i 14.992, 14.993, 14.994, 14.995, 14.996, 14.997, 14.998, 14.999, 15.000, 15.001, 15.002, 15.003, 15.004

j 29.05, 29.06, 29.07, 29.08, 29.09, 29.10, 29.11, 29.12, 29.13, 29.14, 29.15, 29.16

Refresher

l a 3.4, 3.44, 3.45, 3.5, 3.54, 3.55
b 7.19, 7.2, 7.26, 7.27, 7.3, 7.62
c 9.1, 9.11, 9.18, 9.19, 9.2, 9.28
d 4.18, 4.68, 4.8, 4.86, 4.9, 4.92
e 1.07, 1.17, 1.7, 1.71, 1.75, 1.77
f 2.1, 2.49, 2.5, 2.58, 2.73, 2.8
g 5.1, 5.18, 5.46, 5.49, 5.64, 5.8
h 12.2, 12.48, 12.62, 12.8, 12.84, 12.9
i 24.17, 24.5, 24.7, 24.75, 24.9, 24.93
j 48.05, 48.2, 48.25, 48.3, 48.5, 48.55
k 33.03, 33.28, 33.3, 33.6, 33.8, 33.82
l 18.02, 18.09, 18.2, 18.29, 18.9, 18.92
m 71.06, 71.4, 71.48, 71.6, 71.8, 71.86
n 48.1, 48.29, 48.6, 48.72, 48.73, 48.99
o 36.03, 36.1, 36.3, 36.72, 36.82, 36.9

Challenge

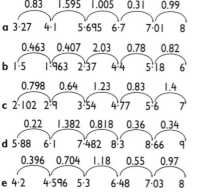

a 3·27 — 0.83, 4·1 — 1.595, 5·695 — 1.005, 6·7 — 0.31, 7·01 — 0.99, 8

b 1·5 — 0.463, 1·963 — 0.407, 2·37 — 2.03, 4·4 — 0.78, 5·18 — 0.82, 6

c 2·102 — 0.798, 2·9 — 0.64, 3·54 — 1.23, 4·77 — 0.83, 5·6 — 1.4, 7

d 5·88 — 0.22, 6·1 — 1.382, 7·482 — 0.818, 8·3 — 0.36, 8·66 — 0.34, 9

e 4·2 — 0.396, 4·596 — 0.704, 5·3 — 1.18, 6·48 — 0.55, 7·03 — 0.97, 8

Week 4, Lesson 5 – Pages 38 and 39

Practice

Open

Refresher

l a 7 b 6 c 4 d 9 e 8
  f 7 g 3 h 7 i 9 j 5
2 a 2.4 b 1.1 c 5.7 d 2.5 e 7.5
  f 6.3 g 4.9 h 2.0 i 3.8 j 7.6

Challenge

a 7.2 b 6.3 c 7.5 d 3.0 e 4.0
f 8.4 g 6.7 h 3.0 i 9.8 j 1.5

Week 5, Lesson 1 – Pages 40 and 41

Practice

l

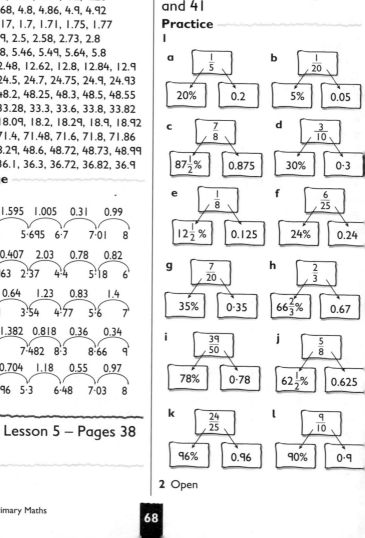

a $\frac{1}{5}$ → 20%, 0.2
b $\frac{1}{20}$ → 5%, 0.05
c $\frac{7}{8}$ → $87\frac{1}{2}\%$, 0.875
d $\frac{3}{10}$ → 30%, 0·3
e $\frac{1}{8}$ → $12\frac{1}{2}\%$, 0.125
f $\frac{6}{25}$ → 24%, 0.24
g $\frac{7}{20}$ → 35%, 0·35
h $\frac{2}{3}$ → $66\frac{2}{3}\%$, 0.67
i $\frac{39}{50}$ → 78%, 0·78
j $\frac{5}{8}$ → $62\frac{1}{2}\%$, 0.625
k $\frac{24}{25}$ → 96%, 0.96
l $\frac{9}{10}$ → 90%, 0·9

2 Open

Refresher

Fraction	Decimal	Percentage
a $\frac{1}{2}$	$1 \div 2 = 0.5$	$100 \div 2 = 50\%$
b $\frac{1}{4}$	$1 \div 4 = 0.25$	$100 \div 4 = 25\%$
c $\frac{1}{5}$	$1 \div 5 = 0.2$	$100 \div 5 = 20\%$
d $\frac{1}{3}$	$1 \div 3 = 0.33$	$100 \div 3 = 33\frac{1}{3}\%$
e $\frac{1}{8}$	$1 \div 8 = 0.125$	$100 \div 8 = 12\frac{1}{2}\%$
f $\frac{1}{10}$	$1 \div 10 = 0.1$	$100 \div 10 = 10\%$
g $\frac{1}{100}$	$1 \div 100 = 0.01$	$100 \div 100 = 1\%$
h $\frac{3}{4}$	$1 \div 4 = 0.25$	$100 \div 4 = 25\%$
	$0.25 \times 3 = 0.75$	$25\% \times 3 = 75\%$

Challenge
Open

Week 5, Lesson 2 – Pages 42 and 43

Practice

a

60p	£3.60

£12

12p	£8.40

b

8	4

32

16	3.2

c

8	48

80

60	24

d

140	350

1400

70	175

e

£28	£56

£560

£70	£5.60

f

£36.20	£72.40

£362

£325.80	£253.40

g

£85	£212.50

£850

£637.50	£425

h

11	1100

1100

55	330

Refresher

a 50%	b 50%	c $33\frac{1}{3}\%$
d 20%	e 25%	f $12\frac{1}{2}\%$
g 50%	h 10%	i 20%
j 10%	k 75%	

Challenge
1 Answers will vary
2 Answers will vary

Week 5, Lesson 3 – Pages 44 and 45

Practice

1	Monday	Tuesday	Wednesday	Thursday	Friday
a	£13.50	£12.75	£10.50	£7.50	£3.75
b	£24.84	£23.46	£19.32	£13.80	£6.90
c	£40.50	£38.25	£31.50	£22.50	£11.25
d	£28.80	£27.20	£22.40	£16	£8
e	£45.90	£43.35	£35.70	£25.50	£12.75
f	£57.06	£53.89	£44.38	£31.70	£15.85

2a 10% **b** 20% **c** $33\frac{1}{3}\%$
   d $12\frac{1}{2}\%$ **e** 5%

Refresher

	Monday	Tuesday	Wednesday	Thursday	Friday
Book	£4.68	£4.16	£3.64	£2.60	£1.30
Tape	£1.80	£1.60	£1.40	£1	50p
Pencils	£3.42	£3.04	£2.66	£1.90	95p
Card	£1.62	£1.44	£1.26	90p	45p
Notebook	£2.34	£2.08	£1.82	£1.30	65p
Pencil case	£3.60	£3.20	£2.80	£2	£1

Challenge
Open

Week 5, Lesson 4 – Pages 46 and 47

Practice
1 a Ratio is 1 : 2
   Proportion is 1 in every 3
   $\frac{1}{3}$ are shaded green
   Smaller shape is $\frac{1}{2}$ the size of the larger

Collins Primary Maths

b Ratio is 1 : 3
Proportion is 1 in every 4
$\frac{1}{4}$ are shaded green
Smaller shape is $\frac{1}{3}$ the size of the larger
c Ratio is 1 : 3
Proportion is 1 in every 4
$\frac{1}{4}$ are shaded green
Smaller shape is $\frac{1}{3}$ the size of the larger
d Ratio is 1 : 3
Proportion is 1 in every 4
$\frac{1}{4}$ are shaded green
Smaller shape is $\frac{1}{3}$ the size of the larger
e Ratio is 1 : 5
Proportion is 1 in every 6
$\frac{1}{6}$ are shaded green
Smaller shape is $\frac{1}{5}$ the size of the larger
f Ratio is 1 : 6
Proportion is 1 in every 7
$\frac{1}{7}$ are shaded green
Smaller shape is $\frac{1}{6}$ the size of the larger
g Ratio is 1 : 10
Proportion is 1 in every 11
$\frac{1}{11}$ are shaded green
Smaller shape is $\frac{1}{10}$ the size of the larger
h Ratio is 1 : 5
Proportion is 1 in every 6
$\frac{1}{6}$ are shaded green
Smaller shape is $\frac{1}{5}$ the size of the larger
i Ratio is 1 : 4
Proportion is 1 in every 5
$\frac{1}{5}$ are shaded green
Smaller shape is $\frac{1}{4}$ the size of the larger

Refresher

a ratio is 2 : 1, proportion is 2 in every 3
b ratio is 3 : 1, proportion is 3 in every 4
c ratio is 1 : 1, proportion is 1 in every 2
d ratio is 2 : 3, proportion is 2 in every 5
e ratio is 4 : 3, proportion is 4 in every 7

Challenge

Answers will vary

Week 5, Lesson 5 – Pages 48 and 49

Practice

1 a 1 : 3   **b** 1 out of every 4
  c 3 out of every 4 **d** 12
  e 24
2 a 2 : 5   **b** 2 in every 7
  c 5 in every 7   **d** 10
  e 6
3 a 3 : 5   **b** 3 in every 8
  c 5 in every 8   **d** 40
  e 64
4 a 3 : 1   **b** 3 l in every 4 l
  c 1 l in every 4 l   **d** $2\frac{1}{2}$ l
  e 16 l

Refresher

1 a 40 m   **b** 240 m
  c 240 m and 60 m
2 a 12 days   **b** 10 days
  c 12 days of rain, 18 days of sun
3 a £1.60   **b** £1
  c £4 spent, £2 saved

Challenge

1 a 1 in every 5   **b** 4 in every 5
  c 1 : 4
2 a $\frac{3}{5}$ **b** $\frac{2}{5}$ **c** 2 : 3
3 a $\frac{2}{3}$ **b** $\frac{1}{3}$ **c** 2 : 1

Week 6, Lesson 1 – Pages 50 and 51

Practice

1 a 26 **b** $\frac{4}{13}$ **c** $\frac{3}{13}$ **d** $\frac{3}{26}$ **e** $\frac{6}{13}$
2 a 45 **b** $\frac{2}{9}$ **c** $\frac{1}{3}$ **d** $\frac{1}{9}$ **e** $\frac{11}{45}$
3 a

Pets	Homes
0	9
1	12
2	9
3	6
Total	36

b $\frac{1}{4}$

4 a

Bedrooms	Houses
1	4
2	16
3	8
4	12
Total	40

b $\frac{1}{5}$

Collins Primary Maths

70

Refresher

1 a $\frac{2}{10} = \frac{1}{5}$ b $\frac{5}{10} = \frac{1}{2}$ c $\frac{7}{10}$
  d $\frac{4}{10} = \frac{2}{5}$ e $\frac{8}{10} = \frac{4}{5}$
2 a $\frac{3}{12} = \frac{1}{4}$ b $\frac{4}{12} = \frac{1}{3}$ c $\frac{6}{12} = \frac{1}{2}$
  d $\frac{5}{12}$ e $\frac{8}{12} = \frac{2}{3}$

Challenge

1 a Maybury Road b Maybury Road
  c Greenfield Close d Greenfield Close
2 a $\frac{4}{10}$
  b Maybury Close has more ($\frac{13}{20}$)

Week 6, Lesson 2 – Pages 52 and 53

Practice

Answers will vary

Refresher

1 a 45% b 70% c 85% d 30%
  e 60% f 40% g 16% h 90%
  i 52% j 84%
2 a 29% b 47% c 79% d 78%
  e 9%   f 23% g 71% h 61%
  i 78% j 31%

Challenge

1
Party	Votes	Percentage
Labour	10	25%
Conservative	8	20%
Liberal Democrat	18	45%
Others	4	10%
Total	40	

2
Party	Votes	Percentage
Labour	24	40%
Conservative	9	15%
Liberal Democrat	21	35%
Others	6	10%
Total	60	

Week 6, Lesson 3 – Pages 54 and 55

Practice

1
Item	Fraction	Money spent (£)
books	$\frac{1}{5}$	£6
handbags	$\frac{2}{5}$	£12
clothes	$\frac{2}{5}$	£12
Total		£30

Item	Fraction	Money spent (£)
computer game	$\frac{1}{5}$	£13
clothes	$\frac{2}{5}$	£26
bicycle wheel	$\frac{3}{10}$	£19.50
magazines	$\frac{1}{10}$	£6.50
Total		£65

2 a
Item	Fraction	Money spent (£)
guest house	$\frac{1}{3}$	£273
entertainment	$\frac{2}{9}$	£182
eating out	$\frac{1}{9}$	£91
car hire	$\frac{1}{3}$	£273
Total		£819

b
Item	Fraction	Money spent (£)
caravan sites	$\frac{1}{5}$	£148
entertainment	$\frac{1}{5}$	£148
fuel	$\frac{3}{10}$	£222
food etc.	$\frac{3}{10}$	£222
Total		£740

Refresher

Jane's books
Book	Fraction	Money spent (£)
space	$\frac{1}{2}$	£12
horses	$\frac{1}{4}$	£6
puzzles	$\frac{1}{8}$	£3
magazines	$\frac{1}{8}$	£3
Total		£24

Ken's books
Book	Fraction	Money spent (£)
adventure	$\frac{1}{3}$	£6
computers	$\frac{1}{6}$	£3
history	$\frac{1}{2}$	£9
Total		£18

Collins Primary Maths

Challenge

1 a

Item	Money spent (£)	Fraction
Geometry set	2	$\frac{1}{4}$
Sweets	1	$\frac{1}{8}$
Cinema	3	$\frac{3}{8}$
Magazine	2	$\frac{1}{4}$
Total	£8	

b

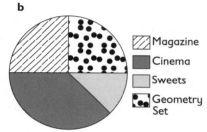

- ▨ Magazine
- ■ Cinema
- ▨ Sweets
- ● Geometry Set

2

a

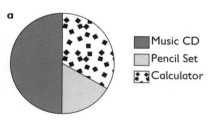

- ■ Music CD
- □ Pencil Set
- ● Calculator

b

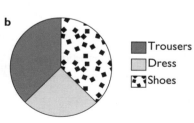

- ■ Trousers
- □ Dress
- ● Shoes

Practice

1 Ben's fish

Fish	Percentage %
Angel	$33\frac{1}{3}$
Goldfish	$33\frac{1}{3}$
Guppy	$33\frac{1}{3}$

Larry's fish

Fish	Percentage %
Angel	10
Goldfish	30
Guppy	60

Gurjit's fish

Fish	Percentage %
Angel	$12\frac{1}{2}$
Goldfish	25
Guppy	$62\frac{1}{2}$

2 a Gurjit   **b** Ben   **c** Larry
d 75%   **e** $66\frac{2}{3}$%   **f** Gurjit

3

Animal	Percentage %
Cow	29
Sheep	29
Chicken	43

a 58%   **b** 72%   **c** 14%

Refresher

1 a

Animal	Percentage %
Cats	30
Dogs	40
Hamsters and Rabbits	10
Others	20

b 70%   **c** 50%   **d** 60%

2 a

Animal	Percentage %
Donkeys	20
Horses	60
Others	20

b 80%   **c** 40%   **d** 20%

Challenge

1 Myrna's garden

Bird	Percentage %
Thrush	11
Starling	33
Blackbird	33
Other	23
Total	100

Wayne's garden

Bird	Percentage %
Thrush	8
Starling	42
Blackbird	16
Other	34
Total	100

Kim's garden

Bird	Percentage %
Thrush	16
Starling	25
Blackbird	42
Other	17
Total	100

2 a Kim   **b** Kim

Week 6, Lesson 5 – Pages 58 and 59

Practice

1 a
Miranda hotel residents

Age	Number	Percentage (%)
up to 21	30	10
22–39	150	50
40 and over	120	40

Compton hotel residents

Age	Number	Percentage (%)
up to 21	108	60
22–39	36	20
40 and over	36	20

b Compton, because there is a large percentage of residents up to 21 years of age

c 90%

d 80%

2
Harpley Bus Station

Employee	Number	Percentage (%)
Driver	35	50
Inspector	7	10
Mechanic	14	20
Other	14	20

Fizz Drinks Company

Employee	Number	Percentage (%)
Factory	100	40
Delivery	75	30
Sales	50	20
Management	25	10

3 a $3 \times 12 = 36$ **b** 12   **c** $4 \times 12 = 48$

Refresher
Templeton Estate

Size of family	Number
1 or 2	6
3	6
4	24
over 4	12

Sidbury Grange

Size of family	Number
1 or 2	20
3	40
4	60
over 4	80

Challenge

1

- 60 and over
- 40–59
- 20–39
- Under 20

2 a

- 60 and over
- 40–59
- 20–39
- Under 20

b

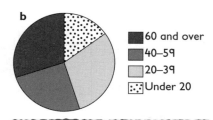

- 60 and over
- 40–59
- 20–39
- Under 20

Week 7, Lesson 1 – Pages 60 and 61

Practice

Answers will vary

Refresher

Answers will vary

Challenge

Answers will vary

Week 7, Lesson 2 – Pages 62 and 63

Practice

1–4 Modal Class: 20–29 year olds

Age	Tally	Frequency	Percentage
10–19	‖‖ ‖‖ ‖‖	13	24
20–29	‖‖ ‖‖ ‖‖ ‖	16	30
30–39	‖‖ ‖‖	7	13
40–49	‖‖ ‖‖‖	8	15
50–59	‖‖ ‖	6	11
60–69	‖‖‖	3	6
70–79	‖	1	2
Total frequency		54	

5 a 54%   b 19%   c 28%   d 40%

6   **Ages of people when they passed their driving tests**

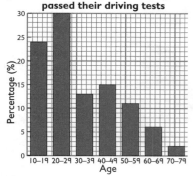

Refresher

1–2

Times abroad	Tally	Total
0–4	‖‖ ‖‖ ‖‖	15
5–9	‖‖ ‖‖ ‖	11
10–14	‖‖ ‖	6
15–19	‖‖‖	4
20–24	‖	2
25–29	‖	2

1 Modal class: 0–4 times abroad.
   Greatest number of people.

3 a 32   b 4   c 10

4   **Number of people who travelled abroad in the last 5 years**

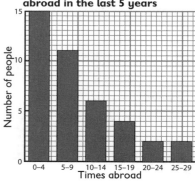

Challenge

1 a adults

   b 22% of adults and of children

Week 7, Lesson 3 – Pages 64 and 65

Practice

1

Science Test Results

Score	Number of children	Percentage
1–5	10	12.5%
6–10	10	12.5%
11–15	20	25%
16–20	30	37.5%
21–25	10	12.5%
Total	80	

2a 25% **b** 75% **c** 62.5%
d 37.5% **e** 16–20

3

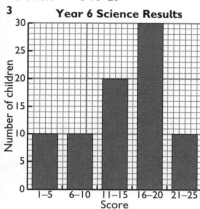

Year 6 Science Results

4a
History Test Results

Score	Number of children	Percentage
1–5	24	10%
6–10	48	20%
11–15	90	37.5%
16–20	48	20%
21–25	30	12.5%
Total	240	

b Answers will vary. Typical answer: 70% of children scored over 10 in history compared with 75% in science.

Refresher

I Gary's Results

Score	Percentage
1–10	10%
11–20	20%
21–30	30%
31–40	10%
41–50	30%
Total	100%

2a 90% **b** 30% **c** 70% **d** 50%
e 21–30 and 41–50

3

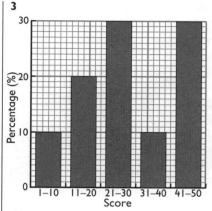

Challenge

I

Score	Number of batsmen	Percentage
0–19	6	5%
20–39	18	15%
40–59	42	35%
60–79	36	30%
80–99	18	15%
Total	120	

2

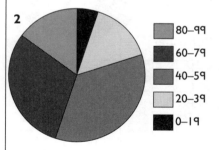

- 80–99
- 60–79
- 40–59
- 20–39
- 0–19

Collins Primary Maths

Week 8, Lesson 1 – Pages 66 and 67

Practice

1

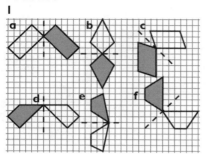

2

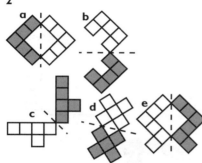

Refresher

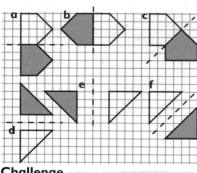

Challenge

1

2 Open

Week 8, Lesson 2 – Pages 68 and 69

Practice

Open

Refresher

1 a

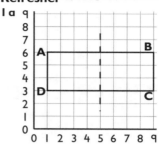

b B = (9, 6), C = (9, 3)

2 a

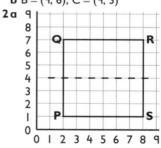

b Q = (2, 7), R = (8, 7)

3 a

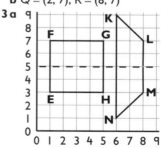

b F = (1, 7), G = (5, 7)

4 a See 3a above.

b M = (8, 3), N = (6, 1)

Challenge

Open

Week 8, Lesson 3 – Pages 70 and 71

Practice

a

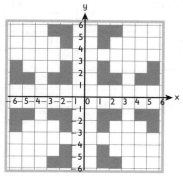

b

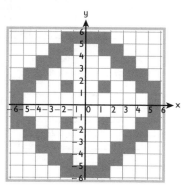

c

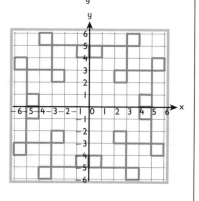

d

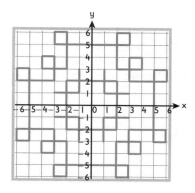

Refresher

1–3

a

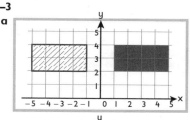

b

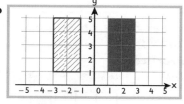

c

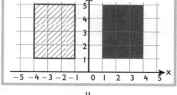

d

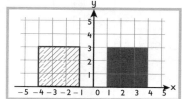

Collins Primary Maths

a (−1, 2), (−5, 2), (−1, 4), (−5, 4)
b (−1, 1), (−3, 1), (−1, 5), (−3, 5)
c (−1, 1), (−4, 1), (−1, 5), (−4, 5)
d (−1, 0), (−4, 0), (−1, 3), (−4, 3)

Challenge

1

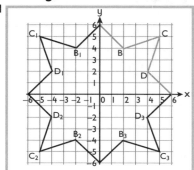

2

1st quadrant	2nd quadrant	3rd quadrant	4th quadrant
B = (2, 4)	B_1 = (−2, 4)	B_2 = (−2, −4)	B_3 = (2, −4)
C = (5, 5)	C_1 = (−5, 5)	C_2 = (−5, −5)	C_3 = (5, −5)
D = (4, 2)	D_1 = (−4, 2)	D_2 = (−4, −2)	D_3 = (4, −2)

Week 8, Lesson 4 – Pages 72 and 73

Practice

1–2

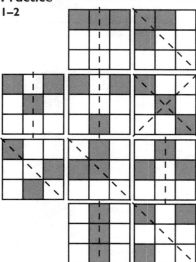

3

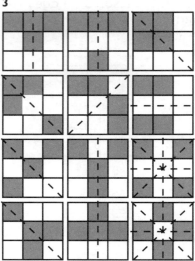

4–5

Number of blue squares	Number of flags
1	3
2	6
3	10
4	12
5	12
6	10
7	6
8	3

Refresher

1–2

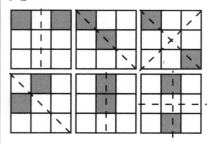

Challenge

The variations for 2 blue, 1 yellow and 1 green are:

B	B
Y	G

+ 3 Rotations = 4

B	B
G	Y

+ 3 Rotations = 4

B	G		Y	B		B	Y		G	B
Y	B		B	G		G	B		B	Y

= 4

Total number of variations = 12
2G + 1B + 1Y: total 12
2Y + 1B + 1G: total 12
Total number of different flags 36

Week 8, Lesson 5 – Pages 74 and 75

Open

Week 9, Lesson 1 – Pages 76 and 77

Practice

Open

Refresher

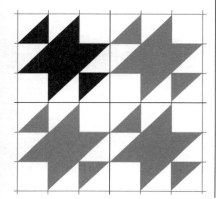

Week 9, Lesson 2 – Pages 78 and 79

Practice

1 a 4	b 4	c 2	d 3	e 4
f 7	g 5	h 4	i 1	j 2
k 4	l 3	m 4		

Refresher

1

2 Open

Challenge

Open

Week 9, Lesson 3 – Pages 80 and 81

Open

Week 9, Lesson 4 – Pages 82 and 83

Practice

1 a 6   b 5 houses: 10
                 6 houses: 15
                 7 houses: 21

2

Number of houses	Number of intersections
2	1
3	3
4	6
5	10
6	15
7	21

3 10 homes: 45

Refresher

Open

Challenge

8 airports: 28
10 airports: 45

Collins Primary Maths

Week 9, Lesson 5 – Pages 84 and 85

Practice

2

a Number of intersecting roads	b Number of intersection points	c Total number of post codes needed
2	1	4
3	3	9
4	6	16
5	10	25
6	15	36
7	21	49
8	28	64
9	36	81
10	45	100

3 b triangular numbers

c square numbers

Refresher

1

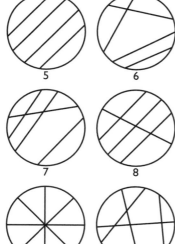

10

11

Challenge

Maximum number of regions = 31

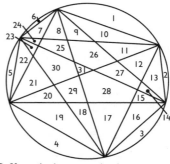

NB: If pupils draw regular hexagons then the flower bed in the centre will be lost.

Week 10, Lesson 1 – Pages 86 and 87

Practice

1 a 180 min = 3 h

b 205 min = 3 h 25 min

c 205 min = 3 h 25 min

d 90 min = 1 h 30 min

e 180 min = 3 h

f 180 min = 3 h

2

Type of meat	Weight of meat	Roasting time in oven in minutes	Time meat is put into oven
Beef	6 kg	260	12:40 p.m.
Lamb	5 kg	280	12:20 p.m.
Pork	4·5 kg	295	12:05 p.m.
Chicken	5 kg	165	2:15 p.m.
Turkey	6 kg	260	12:40 p.m.
Duck	4 kg	270	12:30 p.m.

Refresher

1

Cooking time in minutes	Weight in kilograms						
	0·5	1	1·5	2	2·5	3	3·5
Lamb	30	60	90	120	150	180	210
Chicken	20	40	60	80	100	120	140

2 5:40 p.m.

3 2 kg

Challenge

1

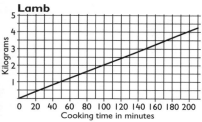

Lamb

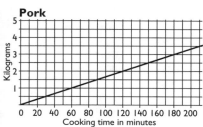

Pork

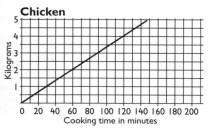

Chicken

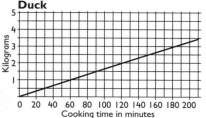

Duck

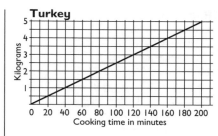

Turkey

2 3 kg beef = 120 min plus 20 min = 2 h 20 min

3 kg lamb = 150 min plus 30 min = 3 h

3 kg pork = 180 min plus 25 min = 3 h 25 min

3 kg chicken = 90 min plus 15 min = 1 h 45 min

3 kg duck = 180 min plus 30 min = 3 h 30 min

3 kg turkey = 120 min plus 20 min = 2 h 20 min

Week 10, Lesson 2 – Pages 88 and 89

Practice

1

Litres	Millilitres	Centilitres
1·5 l	1500 ml	150 cl
2·25 l	2250 ml	225 cl
3·6 l	3600 ml	360 cl
3.26 l	3260 ml	326 cl
5.08 l	5080 ml	508 cl
0.75 l	750 ml	75 cl
1.05 l	1050 ml	105 cl

2 a (i) A + C = 7.365 l
  (ii) A + B = 7.375 l
  (iii) A + D = 10.625 l
  b (i) B and C = 0.01 l
   (ii) B and D = 3.25 l
  c 2.375 l   **d** D   **e** 12.375 l
  f 162 cl   **g** 1950 ml

Collins Primary Maths

Refresher

1 1 litre = 1000 ml
   1 litre = 100 cl
   1 centilitre = 10 ml
2 a 5 cl   b 50 cl   c 75 cl   d 100 cl
  e 8 cl   f 9 cl   g 44 cl   h 200 cl
3 a 100 ml   b 1000 ml   c 250 ml
  d 50 ml   e 370 ml   f 980 ml
  g 4000 ml   h 40 ml

Challenge

1 E, A, C, D, B
2 A = 75 cl
   B = 10 cl
   C = 50 cl
   D = 25 cl
   E = 100 cl

Week 10, Lesson 3 – Page 90 and 91

Practice

1 a 2500 ml, 250 cl   b 2250 ml, 225 cl
  c 2050 ml 205 cl   d 520 ml, 52 cl
  e 5020 ml, 502 cl   f 25 000 ml, 2500 cl
2 a 765 cl, 7.65 l   b 56 cl, 0.56 l
  c 2 cl, 0.02 l   d 507 cl, 5.07 l
  e 70 cl, 0.7 l   f 7 cl, 0.07 l
3

a

Amount	Rounded to nearest	
	$\frac{1}{10}$ litre	litre
2·25 l	2·3 l	2 l
3·706 l	3·7 l	4 l
6·088 l	6·1 l	6 l
7·990 l	8·0 l	8 l

b

Amount	Rounded to nearest	
	$\frac{1}{10}$ litre	litre
530 ml	0·5 l	1 l
818 ml	0·8 l	1 l
4420 ml	4·4 l	4 l
690 ml	0·7 l	1 l

4 a 600 ml

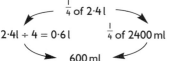

$\frac{1}{4}$ of 2·4 l

2·4 l ÷ 4 = 0·6 l $\frac{1}{4}$ of 2400 ml

600 ml

  b 800 ml   c 3800 ml   d 1900 ml
5 a True   b False   c True
  d False   e False   f True

Refresher

1 a 6 ml   b 600 ml   c 60 ml
  d 60 ml   e 6000 ml   f 6000 ml
2 $\frac{3}{4}$ l = 0.75 l
   0.8 l = 800 ml
   5.6 l = 5600 ml
   300 ml = 0.3 l
   3400 ml = 3.4 l
   600 ml = 0.6 l

Challenge

a 10 l   9.001 l
   8.002 l   7.003 l
   6.004 l   5.005 l
   4.006 l   3.007 l
   2.008 l   1.009 l
   0.010 l
b 1 l   0.89 l
   0.78 l   0.67 l
   0.56 l   0.45 l
   0.34 l   0.23 l
   0.12 l   0.01 l

Week 10, Lesson 4 – Pages 92 and 93

Practice

1 a 9 l   b 14 l   c 18 l
  d 36 l   e 4 l   f 8 l
2 a 1.6 gallons   b 2.2 gallons
  c 3.1 gallons   d 10.0 gallons
  e 4.9 gallons   f 6.0 gallons
3 a 240 pints   b 30 gallons
  c 135 litres
4 16 pints

Refresher

1 a 7 pints   **b** 8 pints
  c $4\frac{1}{2}$ pints   **d** $3\frac{1}{2}$ pints
2 a 0.6 l   **b** 1.4 l
  c 3.6 l   **d** 4.6 l

Challenge

Fiat Punto: 46 l
Ford Fiesta: 39 l or 40 l
Rover 25: 50 l
Toyota Yaris: 44 l
VW Polo: 44 l

Week 10, Lesson 5 – Pages 94 and 95

Practice

1

Name	Meter reading in litres		
of boat	before refuelling	after refuelling	litres sold
Sea Hawk	7326 l	7430 l	104 l
Sea Urchin	7430 l	7665 l	235 l
Sea Eagle	7665 l	7934 l	269 l
Sea Farer	7934 l	8481 l	547 l

2 a 1971 l   **b** 219 l
  c Tank 1: 1155 l, Tank 2: 1374 l
3 450 l

Refresher

1 a 10   **b** 5   **c** 12   **d** 50
2 a 36 l   **b** 72 l   **c** 180 l   **d** 900 l

Challenge

1 80 000 kg   **2** 4 litres

Week 11, Lesson 1 – Pages 96 and 97

Practice

Answers will vary

Refresher

1 a $12 + 6 = 18$ **b** $4 + 15 = 19$
  c $9 + 6 = 15$ **d** $7 + 5 = 12$
  e $7 + 7 = 14$ **f** $6 + 1 = 7$
  g $2 + 17 = 19$ **h** $8 + 8 = 16$
  i $9 + 5 = 14$ **j** $13 + 7 = 20$
  k $6 + 3 = 9$ **l** $11 + 6 = 17$
  m $10 + 8 = 18$ **n** $3 + 5 = 8$
  o $4 + 9 = 13$ **p** $8 + 2 = 10$
  q $13 + 4 = 17$ **r** $14 + 0 = 14$

  s $9 + 9 = 18$ **t** $11 + 4 = 15$
  u $12 + 4 = 16$
2 a   365
    $+ 3921$
    $\underline{4286}$
  b $759 + 8541 = 9300$
  c $5962 + 4198 = 10\ 160$
  d $625 + 384 = 1009$
  e $725 + 4593 = 5318$
  f $9607 + 831 = 10\ 438$
  g $5333 + 6248 = 11\ 581$
  h $4930 + 483 = 5413$
  i $7306 + 493 = 7799$
  j $351.8 + 632.7 = 984.5$
  k $6914.2 + 485.7 = 7399.9$
  l $6849.26 + 584.21 = 7433.47$
  m $526.1 + 367.8 = 893.9$
  n $1633.55 + 486.72 = 2120.27$
  o $596.78 + 153.49 = 750.27$
  p $664.95 + 725.88 = 1390.83$

Challenge

For example:
a $2.794 + 0.3 = 3.094$
b $47.03 + 9.2 = 56.23$
c $943 + 70.2 = 1013.2$
d $2.7 + 49.03 = 51.73$
e $907.2 + 43 = 950.2$

Week 11, Lesson 2 – Pages 98 and 99

Practice

Answers will vary

Refresher

1 a $15 - 6 = 9$ **b** $9 - 5 = 4$
  c $17 - 11 = 6$ **d** $12 - 8 = 4$
  e $19 - 9 = 10$ **f** $10 - 6 = 4$
  g $20 - 5 = 15$ **h** $13 - 8 = 5$
  i $9 - 9 = 0$ **j** $18 - 13 = 5$
  k $14 - 11 = 3$ **l** $16 - 3 = 13$
  m $16 - 7 = 9$ **n** $8 - 3 = 5$
  o $12 - 7 = 5$ **p** $18 - 9 = 9$
  q $20 - 12 = 8$ **r** $19 - 18 = 1$
  s $5 - 0 = 5$ **t** $15 - 7 = 8$
  u $19 - 6 = 13$

Collins Primary Maths

2 a 4835
   −1256
   ‾‾‾‾
   3579

b $842 - 351 = 491$
c $7802 - 3657 = 4145$
d $19\,873 - 523 = 19\,350$
e $14\,932 - 7521 = 7411$
f $6388 - 921 = 5467$
g $71\,952 - 825 = 71\,127$
h $77\,604 - 15\,402 = 62\,202$
i $95\,317 - 4526 = 90\,791$
j $782.3 - 51.9 = 730.4$
k $485.12 - 96.43 = 388.69$
l $455.9 - 122.4 = 333.5$
m $6933.5 - 42.8 = 6890.7$
n $78.56 - 24.99 = 53.57$
o $653.56 - 81.59 = 571.97$
p $6214.87 - 591.06 = 5623.81$

Challenge

a $61.5 - 34.2 = 27.3$
b $6.35 - 4.21 = 2.14$
c $43.52 - 1.6 = 41.92$
d $31.4 - 2.56 = 28.84$
e $135.2 - 46 = 89.2$
f $6.42 - 5.13 = 1.29$

Week 11, Lesson 3 – Pages 100 and 101

Practice

1 a $73 + 24 = 97$ **b** $97 + 58 = 155$
   $73 - 24 = 49$ $97 - 58 = 39$
c $93 + 38 = 131$ **d** $62 + 28 = 90$
   $93 - 38 = 55$ $62 - 28 = 34$
e $77 + 54 = 131$ **f** $61 + 38 = 99$
   $77 - 54 = 23$ $61 - 38 = 23$
g $99 + 87 = 186$ **h** $14 + 67 = 81$
   $99 - 87 = 12$ $67 - 14 = 53$
i $86 + 49 = 135$ **j** $83 + 49 = 132$
   $86 - 49 = 37$ $83 - 49 = 34$
k $19 + 89 = 108$ **l** $51 + 17 = 68$
   $89 - 19 = 70$ $51 - 17 = 34$
m $59 + 47 = 106$ **n** $25 + 92 = 117$
   $59 - 47 = 12$ $92 - 25 = 67$
o $47 + 88 = 135$ **p** $42 + 91 = 133$
   $88 - 47 = 41$ $91 - 42 = 49$

q $37 + 55 = 92$ **r** $29 + 39 = 68$
   $55 - 37 = 18$ $39 - 29 = 10$
s $96 + 29 = 125$ **t** $84 + 21 = 105$
   $96 - 29 = 67$ $84 - 21 = 63$

Refresher

1 a $49 + 27 = 76$ **b** $37 + 84 = 121$
c $71 + 21 = 92$ **d** $93 + 44 = 137$
e $58 + 32 = 90$ **f** $76 + 47 = 123$
g $29 + 19 = 48$ **h** $37 + 73 = 110$
i $26 + 67 = 93$ **j** $82 + 37 = 119$
k $86 - 31 = 55$ **l** $74 - 29 = 45$
m $95 - 36 = 59$ **n** $78 - 49 = 29$
o $66 - 23 = 43$ **p** $71 - 59 = 12$
q $97 - 48 = 49$ **r** $63 - 14 = 49$
s $55 - 27 = 28$ **t** $88 - 41 = 47$

2 a $59 + 26 = 85$
   $590 + 260 = 850$
   $5900 + 2600 = 8500$
b $48 + 21 = 69$
   $480 + 210 = 690$
   $4800 + 2100 = 6900$
c $72 + 68 = 140$
   $720 + 680 = 1400$
   $7200 + 6800 = 14\,000$
d $57 + 29 = 86$
   $570 + 290 = 860$
   $5700 + 2900 = 8600$
e $88 + 51 = 139$
   $880 + 510 = 1390$
   $8800 + 5100 = 13\,900$
f $62 + 91 = 153$
   $620 + 910 = 1530$
   $6200 + 9100 = 15\,300$
g $91 - 35 = 56$
   $910 - 350 = 560$
   $9100 - 3500 = 5600$
h $74 - 18 = 56$
   $740 - 180 = 560$
   $7400 - 1800 = 5600$
i $52 - 31 = 21$
   $520 - 310 = 210$
   $5200 - 3100 = 2100$
j $69 - 48 = 21$
   $690 - 480 = 210$
   $6900 - 4800 = 2100$

k $37 - 12 = 25$
  $370 - 120 = 250$
  $3700 - 1200 = 2500$

Challenge
Open

Week 11, Lesson 4 – Pages 102 and 103

Practice
a $50 + 30 + 80 + 40 = 200$
b $40 + 70 + 10 + 50 = 170$
c $90 + 50 + 60 + 60 = 260$
d $40 + 60 + 70 + 50 = 220$
e $60 + 80 + 30 + 70 = 240$
f $50 + 10 + 90 + 80 = 230$
g $70 + 90 + 20 + 30 = 210$
h $20 + 60 + 80 + 80 = 240$
i $30 + 60 + 30 + 90 = 210$
j $50 + 50 + 40 + 10 = 150$
k $80 + 70 + 60 + 50 = 260$
l $60 + 80 + 70 + 10 = 220$
m $50 + 40 + 30 + 70 = 190$
n $56 + 92 + 31 + 47 = 226$
o $63 + 97 + 51 + 62 = 273$
p $72 + 15 + 46 + 29 = 162$
q $99 + 64 + 71 + 52 = 286$
r $28 + 49 + 72 + 33 = 182$
s $49 + 66 + 17 + 38 = 170$
t $67 + 38 + 19 + 88 = 212$
u $49 + 37 + 19 + 55 = 160$
v $72 + 37 + 81 + 69 = 259$
w $49 + 67 + 28 + 39 = 183$
x $82 + 91 + 46 + 37 = 256$
y $19 + 82 + 46 + 47 = 194$

Refresher
1 $0.1 + 0.9$	**2** $0.01 + 0.09$
$0.2 + 0.8$	$0.02 + 0.08$
$0.3 + 0.7$	$0.03 + 0.07$
$0.4 + 0.6$	$0.04 + 0.06$
$0.5 + 0.5$	$0.05 + 0.05$

3 $4.5 + 5.5$
  $6.3 + 3.7$
  $2.1 + 7.9$
  $9.6 + 0.4$
  $8.8 + 1.2$
  $7.3 + 2.7$

Challenge
For example:
a $(50 \times 4) + 9 + 2 + 1 = 212$
b $(70 \times 4) + 4 + 6 + 8 = 298$
c $(60 \times 4) + 6 + 4 + 9 = 259$
d $(20 \times 4) + 1 + 2 + 3 = 86$
e $(80 \times 4) + 4 + 9 + 7 = 340$
f $(30 \times 4) + 9 + 4 + 5 = 138$
g $(10 \times 4) + 6 + 4 + 8 = 58$
h $(40 \times 4) + 7 + 9 + 8 = 184$
i $(90 \times 4) + 9 + 6 + 4 = 379$
j $(20 \times 4) + 5 + 6 + 15 = 106$

Week 11, Lesson 5

Practice
1 £10.23	**2** £12 480.75
3 1276	**4** 5968
5 £48.74	**6** 561, 239

Refresher
1 £8.41	**2** £10.32
3 48	**4** £38.30
5 £208	**6** 375

Challenge
Open

Week 12, Lesson 1 – Pages 106 and 107

Practice
1 a 1.0	**b** 0.7	**c** 2.0	**d** 1.1
e 2.5	**f** 7.0	**g** 3.9	**h** 5.7
i 1.4	**j** 12.5		
2 a 0.4	**b** 1.2	**c** 0.7	**d** 1.5
e 1.0	**f** 0.8	**g** 0.3	**h** 1.9
i 6.7	**j** 9.2		
3 a 0.5	**b** 0.75	**c** 2.5	**d** 1.25
e 4.25	**f** 1.0	**g** 2.25	**h** 0.25
i 4.0	**j** 5.75		

Collins Primary Maths

4

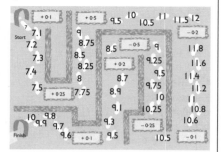

Refresher

l a 1.0, 1.2, 1.4, 1.6, 1.8, 2.0, 2.2, 2.4,
2.6, 2.8, 3.0, 3.2, 3.4

  b 6.5, 6.6, 6.7, 6.8, 6.9, 7.0, 7.1, 7.2,
7.3, 7.4, 7.5, 7.6

  c 7.5, 8.0, 8.5, 9.0, 9.5, 10.0, 10.5, 11.0,
11.5, 12.0, 12.5, 13.0

  d 3.5, 3.75, 4.0, 4.25, 4.5, 4.75, 5.0,
5.25, 5.5, 5.75, 6.0, 6.25

  e 10.5, 10.0, 9.5, 9.0, 8.5, 8.0, 7.5, 7.0,
6.5, 6.0, 5.5, 5.0

  f 9.5, 9.25, 9.0, 8.75, 8.5, 8.25, 8.0,
7.75, 7.5, 7.25, 7.0, 6.75

Challenge

Answers will vary

Week 12, Lesson 2 – Pages 108 and 109

Practice

l a 2, 3	**b** 2, 5	**c** 2, 3, 7
d 2, 3, 5	**e** 5	**f** 2, 7
g 2	**h** 2, 3	**i** 2, 3

2 Factor trees will vary

3 Factor trees will vary

4 a Each number has many different
factors.

  b Each number is the product of the
same prime numbers.

5 a [15 / 3 | 5] **b** [33 / 3 | 11]

c [45 / 3 | 15 / 3 | 5] **d** [21 / 3 | 7]

  e The factor trees are short. The
prime number 3 is common to all
four numbers.

Refresher

Prime: 5, 11, 13, 29, 37, 79

Composite: 9, 15, 18, 20, 24, 26, 44, 45,
54, 57, 69, 88, 90, 100,

Challenge

1 101, 103, 107, 109, 113, 127, 129, 131,
137, 139, 149, 151, 157, 163, 167, 169,
173, 179, 181, 191, 193, 197, 199

2 More between 1 and 100

3 No

Week 12, Lesson 3 – Pages 110 and 111

Practice

1 6, 8, 10, 12, 14, 16, 18, 20, 22, 24, 26, 28,
30, 32, 34, 36, 38, 40, 42, 44, 46, 48, 50

2 Yes

3 Yes, all even numbers above 8 have
more than one solution.

4 48, with 4 pairs

5 Yes, $2 = 1 + 1$ is not a prime number

Refresher

1 41 and 43, 59 and 61, 71 and 73

Challenge

1 5, 7, 9, 11, 13, 15, 17, 19, 21, 23, 25, 27,
29, 31, 33, 35, 37, 39, 41, 43, 45, 47, 49

2 No

3 Odd numbers are only the sum of
two prime numbers where 2 plus a
prime number = odd number.

Week 12, Lesson 4 – Pages 112 and 113

Practice

1 $y = 4$	$y = 13$	$p = 2$	$y = 100$
$n = 4$	$p = 8$	$c = 47$	$n = 12$

2 a $p = 4$ **b** $n = 72$ **c** $y = 42$
  d $n = 54$ **e** $y = 9$ **f** $y = 4$
  g $n = 165$ **h** $p = 14$ **i** $y = 288$
  j $y = 252$ **k** $p = 151$ **l** $y = 10$
  m $n = 48$ **n** $p = 6$

3 a $n - 100 = 25$ **b** $60n = 180$
  c $n + 27 = 84$ **d** $n = 44 \times 4$
  e $n - 52 = 100$

4 a $n = 125$ **b** $n = 3$ **c** $n = 57$
  d $n = 176$ **e** $n = 152$

Refresher

1 a $6 \times 8 = 48$ **b** $27 + 23 = 50$
  c $7 \times 7 = 49$ **d** $100 - 56 = 44$
  e $2 \times 9 + 10 = 28$ **f** $36 \div 4 = 9$

2 a $\frac{1}{2} \times 654 = 327$ **b** $4 \times 50 = 200$
  c $12^2 = 144$ **d** $140 - 129 = 11$
  e $56 \times 3 = 168$ **f** $95 \div 5 = 19$

3 a $72 \div 9 + 2 = 10$ **b** $34 \times 4 = 136$
  c $\frac{1}{2} \times 136 = 68$ **d** $57 \times 100 = 5700$
  e $9300 \div 10 = 930$ **f** $\frac{1}{4} \times 600 = 150$

Challenge

Answers will vary

Week 12, Lesson 5 – Pages 114 and 115

Practice

1 a 3000, 30 000, 300 000, 3 000 000, 30 000 000
   multiply by 10 each time
   Formula $= n \times 10$ or $10n$
  b 102, 108, 114, 120, 126
   add 6 each time
   Formula $= n + 6$
  c 24, 48, 96, 192, 384
   multiply by 2 each time
   Formula $= n \times 2$ or $2n$
  d 761, 751, 741, 731, 721
   subtract 10 each time
   Formula $= n - 10$
  e 54, 162, 486, 1458, 4374
   multiply by 3 each time
   Formula $= n \times 3$ or $3n$
  f 55, 111, 223, 447, 895
   multiply by 2 and add 1 each time

   Formula $= n \times 2 + 1$ or $2n + 1$
  g 1024, 512, 256, 128, 64
   divide by 2 each time
   Formula $= n \div 2$ or $\frac{1}{2} n$ or $\frac{n}{2}$
  h −325, −350, −375, −400, −425
   subtract 25 each time
   Formula $= n - 25$
  i 1.3, 1.5, 1.7, 1.9, 2.1
   add 0.2 each time
   Formula $= n + 0.2$

2 a Cost 12p

n	5	7	12	19	8	25	49	100
T	60p	84p	£1.44	£2.28	96p	£3.00	£5.88	£12.00

  b Cost £22

n	6	9	20	15	11	26	32	50
T	£132	£198	£440	£330	£242	£572	£704	£1100

Refresher

1 a 640, 635, 630, 625, 620
   Formula $= n - 5$
  b 425, 450, 475, 500, 525
   Formula $= n + 25$
  c 18, 54, 162, 486, 1458
   Formula $= n \times 3$ or $3n$
  d 128, 64, 32, 16, 8
   Formula $= n \div 2$ or $\frac{1}{2} n$ or $\frac{n}{2}$
  e 60, 120, 240, 480, 960
   Formula $= n \times 2$ or $2n$

Challenge

Open

Collins Primary Maths

Support Copymasters

Autonal Term (Autumn Term)

SCM 1

a $7 \times 10 = 70$
$7 \times 100 = 700$
b $8 \times 10 = 80$
$8 \times 100 = 800$
c $21 \times 10 = 210$
$21 \times 100 = 2100$
d $38 \times 10 = 380$
$38 \times 100 = 3800$
e $45 \times 10 = 450$
$45 \times 100 = 4500$
f $4200 \div 10 = 420$
$4200 \div 100 = 42$
g $2300 \div 10 = 230$
$2300 \div 100 = 23$
h $8000 \div 10 = 800$
$8000 \div 100 = 80$
i $5100 \div 10 = 510$
$5100 \div 100 = 51$
j $7600 \div 10 = 760$
$7600 \div 100 = 76$
k $9300 \div 10 = 930$
$9300 \div 100 = 93$

SCM 2
Open

SCM 3

a $27 \times 5 =$
$(20 \times 5) + (7 \times 5) =$
$100 + 35 = 135$
b $36 \times 4 = 144$
c $37 \times 3 = 111$
d $32 \times 6 = 192$
e $46 \times 9 = 414$
f $38 \times 8 = 304$
g $24 \times 7 = 168$
h $42 \times 6 = 252$
i $37 \times 9 = 333$
j $28 \times 7 = 196$
k $39 \times 4 = 156$

SCM 4

a

$\times$	300	20	4	
324×5 5	1500	100	20	$= 1620$

b $134 \times 9 = 1206$
c $873 \times 6 = 5238$
d $234 \times 4 = 936$
e $487 \times 2 = 974$
f $1283 \times 4 = 5132$
g $4312 \times 3 = 12936$
h $6314 \times 2 = 12628$
i $2414 \times 5 = 12070$

SCM 5

a

		2	3	4	5
	$\times$				3
(2000×3)	6	0	0	0	
(300×3)		9	0	0	
(40×3)			1	2	0
$5 \times 3)$				1	5
	7	0	3	5	
	1				

b $3624 \times 4 = 14496$
c $2763 \times 5 = 13815$
d $3456 \times 3 = 10368$
e $2926 \times 4 = 11704$
f $4348 \times 3 = 13044$
g $4573 \times 5 = 22865$
h $5336 \times 6 = 32016$

SCM 6

a Improper fraction $\frac{3}{2}$
Mixed number $1\frac{1}{2}$
b Improper fraction $\frac{7}{6}$
Mixed number $1\frac{1}{6}$
c Improper fraction $\frac{5}{3}$
Mixed number $1\frac{2}{3}$
d Improper fraction $\frac{8}{5}$
Mixed number $1\frac{3}{5}$
e Improper fraction $\frac{10}{7}$
Mixed number $1\frac{3}{7}$
f Improper fraction $\frac{16}{10}$
Mixed number $1\frac{6}{10}$
g Improper fraction $\frac{11}{8}$
Mixed number $1\frac{3}{8}$

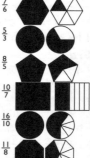

SCM 7

1

a 5 5.1 5.2 5.3 5.4 5.5 5.6 5.7 5.8 5.9 6

b 7 7.1 7.2 7.3 7.4 7.5 7.6 7.7 7.8 7.9 8

c 2 2.1 2.2 2.3 2.4 2.5 2.6 2.7 2.8 2.9 3

d 3 3.1 3.2 3.3 3.4 3.5 3.6 3.7 3.8 3.9 4

e 8 8.1 8.2 8.3 8.4 8.5 8.6 8.7 8.8 8.9 9

2 a 1.4, 4.3, 5.1, 6.8, 7.5, 9.6
  b 4.1, 4.3, 4.5, 4.6, 4.7, 4.9
  c 1.4, 1.5, 1.7, 2.6, 2.8, 2.9,
  d 1.6, 3.7, 6.1, 6.5, 7.2, 7.3
  e 2.8, 3.8, 6.7, 7.9, 8.2, 9.7

3 a 5.9   **b** 4.2   **c** 7.6   **d** 3.7
  e 6.2   **f** 8   **g** 4.8   **h** 5.4
  i 7.8   **j** 8.3

SCM 8

  a 1.4m + 50cm
    1m 40cm + 50cm
    = 1m 90cm
    or 1.9m
  b 1.5m + 30cm
    1m 50cm + 30cm
    = 1m 80cm
    or 1.8m
  c 1.2m + 40cm
    1m 20cm + 40cm
    = 1m 60cm
    or 1.6m
  d 1.1m + 70cm
    1m 10cm + 70cm
    = 1m 80cm
    or 1.8m
  e 1.3m + 20cm
    1m 30cm + 20cm
    = 1m 50cm
    or 1.5m
  f 1.7m + 10cm
    1m 70cm + 10cm
    = 1m 80cm
    or 1.8m
  g 1.9m − 80cm
    1m 90cm − 80cm
    = 1m 10cm
    or 1.1m
  h 1.7m − 50cm
    1m 70cm − 50cm
    = 1m 20cm
    or 1.2m
  i 1.8m − 20cm
    1m 80cm − 20cm
    = 1m 60cm
    or 1.6m

SCM 9

1

Rebecca	Tim
1	2
2	4
3	6
4	8

Rebecca eats 4
Tim eats 8

2

girls	boys
1	3
2	6
3	9
4	12

4 girl cousins
12 boy cousins

3

pencils	felt tips
1	4
2	8
3	12
4	16

4 pencils
16 felt tips

4

Melanie	mum
2	3
4	6
6	9
8	12

Melanie has 8 cakes
Her mum has 12 cakes

SCM 10

1 a Median = 12mm **b** Median = 19mm
  c Median = 12mm **d** Median = 17mm
  e Median = 10mm

2 a 15mm, 20mm, 30mm
    median = 20mm
  b 8mm, 18mm, 21mm, 25mm, 28mm
    median = 21mm
  c 6mm, 9mm, 15mm, 15mm, 18mm,
    20mm, 22mm
    median = 15mm
  d 17mm, 18mm, 20mm, 22mm, 25mm
    median = 20mm
  e 10mm, 15mm, 15mm, 18mm, 18mm,
    21mm, 21mm, 25mm, 30mm
    median = 18mm

Collins Primary Maths

SCM 11

a $6 + 10 = 16$
  $16 \div 2 = 8$
  Mean = 8
b Mean = 11   **c** Mean = 10
d Mean = 24   **e** Mean = 19
f Mean = 8   **g** Mean = 23
h Mean = 19   **i** Mean = 18
j Mean = 7.5   **k** Mean = 4.5
l Mean = 12.5
2a Total = $120\,g + 350\,g = 470\,g$
  Mean = $470 \div 2 = 235\,g$
b Total = 180
  Mean = 90
c Total = 528 cm
  Mean = 264 cm
d Total = 102 cm
  Mean = 51 cm
e Total = 4650 m
  Mean = 2325 m
f Total = £9.84
  Mean = £4.92
g Total = £12
  Mean = £6
h Total = £4183
  Mean = £2091.50
3 a Correct
  b Correct
  c Incorrect, halfway between 5 and
    25 is 15
  d Correct

SCM 12
Open

SCM 13
Open

SCM 14

1 a
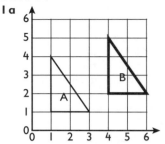
b (4, 2) (4, 5) (6, 2)

2 a
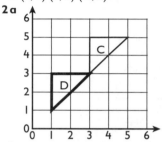
b (1, 1), (1, 3) (3, 3)

3 a
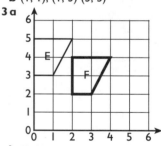
b (2, 2) (2, 4) (4, 4) (3, 2)

4 a
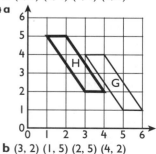
b (3, 2) (1, 5) (2, 5) (4, 2)

SCM 15

1 a

right-angled
isosceles triangle

b

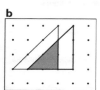

right-angled
isosceles triangle

c

scalene triangle

2a

scalene triangle

b

right-angled
isosceles triangle

c

scalene triangle

3 Open

SCM 16

1 a perimeter = 12 units
  b perimeter = 12 units
  c perimeter = 12 units
2 Open

SCM 17

Open

SCM 18

a	672 − 241 **431**	**b**	849 − 305 **544**	**c**	752 − 341 **411**
d	685 − 342 **343**	**e**	478 − 215 **263**	**f**	687 − 248 **439**
g	941 − 370 **571**	**h**	378 − 129 **249**	**i**	675 − 237 **438**
j	568 − 184 **384**	**k**	749 − 365 **384**	**l**	504 − 323 **181**
m	693 − 526 **167**	**n**	817 − 434 **383**	**o**	748 − 352 **396**
p	437 − 262 **175**	**q**	846 − 382 **464**	**r**	927 − 692 **235**
s	586 − 247 **339**	**t**	973 − 345 **628**		

Collins Primary Maths

SCM 19

1 a 3 packs	b 7 packs	
c 10 packs	d 82 pens	
e 58 pens		
2 a £8.51	b £5.74	c £18.60
d 35p	e £1.14	f £2.13

SCM 20

a	b	c	d
12	0	0	−200
24	15	21	−175
36	30	42	−150
48	45	63	−125
60	60	84	−100
72	75	105	−75
84	90	126	−50
96	105	147	−25
108	120	168	0
120	135	189	25
132	150	210	50
144	165	231	75
156	180	252	100
168	195	273	125
180	210	294	150
192	225	315	175
204	240	336	200
216	255	357	225
228	270	378	250

SCM 21

Answers

Support Copymasters

SCM 22

a 5　　b 5　　c 9　　d 4
e 8　　f 9　　g 11

SCM 23

1 a 1, 3, 9
 b 1, 2, 3, 5, 6, 10, 15, 30
 c 1, 2, 3, 4, 6, 12
 d 1, 3, 5, 15
 e 1, 2, 4, 7, 14, 28
 f 1, 2, 3, 4, 6, 8, 12 24
 g 1, 2, 3, 4, 6, 9, 12, 18, 36
 h 1, 2, 3, 4, 6, 8, 12, 24, 48
 i 1, 2, 4, 7, 8, 14, 28, 56
 j 1, 2, 3, 4, 5, 6, 10, 12, 15, 20, 30, 60

2 a $5 \times 15 = 5 \times 3 \times 5$
$= 15 \times 5$
$= 75$

 b $7 \times 18 = 7 \times 9 \times 2$
$= 63 \times 2$
$= 126$

 c $12 \times 14 = 12 \times 7 \times 2$
$= 84 \times 2$
$= 168$

 d $16 \times 8 = 8 \times 8 \times 2$
$= 64 \times 2$
$= 128$

 e $24 \times 5 = 12 \times 5 \times 2$
$= 60 \times 2$
$= 120$

 f $12 \times 16 = 12 \times 8 \times 2$
$= 96 \times 2$
$= 192$

 g $14 \times 15 = 14 \times 5 \times 3$
$= 70 \times 3$
$= 210$

 h $20 \times 18 = 20 \times 9 \times 2$
$= 180 \times 2$
$= 360$

 i $30 \times 40 = 30 \times 10 \times 4$
$= 300 \times 4$
$= 1200$

 j $20 \times 50 = 20 \times 10 \times 5$
$= 200 \times 5$
$= 1000$

 k $24 \times 15 = 15 \times 12 \times 2$
$= 30 \times 12$
$= 360$

 l $12 \times 22 = 15 \times 12 \times 2$
$= 30 \times 12$
$= 264$

SCM 24

1 a $37 \times 4 = 120 + 28 = 148$
 b $63 \times 5 = 300 + 15 = 315$
 c $28 \times 3 = 60 + 24 = 84$
 d $47 \times 4 = 160 + 28 = 188$
 e $68 \times 3 = 180 + 24 = 204$
2 a $35 \times 6 = 180 + 30 = 210$
 b $72 \times 7 = 490 + 14 = 504$
 c $68 \times 4 = 240 + 32 = 272$
 d $53 \times 8 = 400 + 24 = 424$
 e $29 \times 9 = 180 + 81 = 261$
3 a $38 \times 8 = 240 + 64 = 304$
 b $57 \times 3 = 150 + 21 = 171$
 c $90 \times 5 = 450$
 d $84 \times 6 = 480 + 24 = 504$
 e $37 \times 7 = 210 + 49 = 259$
4 a $56 \times 4 = 200 + 24 = 224$
 b $82 \times 7 = 560 + 14 = 574$
 c $67 \times 9 = 540 + 63 = 603$
 d $58 \times 6 = 300 + 48 = 348$
 e $75 \times 8 = 560 + 40 = 600$
5 a $3 \times 85 = 240 + 15 = 255$
 b $5 \times 93 = 450 + 15 = 465$
 c $8 \times 96 = 720 + 48 = 768$
 d $4 \times 84 = 320 + 16 = 336$
 e $7 \times 69 = 420 + 63 = 483$
6 a $6 \times 75 = 420 + 30 = 450$
 b $9 \times 84 = 720 + 36 = 756$
 c $4 \times 63 = 240 + 12 = 252$
 d $8 \times 79 = 560 + 72 = 632$
 e $7 \times 64 = 420 + 28 = 448$

Collins Primary Maths

SCM 25

1 a $160 \div 8 = 20$ **b** $210 \div 7 = 30$
  c $150 \div 5 = 30$ **d** $200 \div 4 = 50$
  e $120 \div 6 = 20$ **f** $80 \div 4 = 20$
  g $240 \div 3 = 80$ **h** $350 \div 5 = 70$
  i $400 \div 8 = 50$ **j** $270 \div 3 = 90$
  k $360 \div 6 = 60$ **l** $280 \div 7 = 40$
  m $360 \div 9 = 40$ **n** $280 \div 4 = 70$
  o $560 \div 8 = 70$ **p** $540 \div 9 = 60$
  q $420 \div 7 = 60$ **r** $810 \div 9 = 90$

2 a $344 \div 4 \approx 80$ $4\overline{)344}$
      $\underline{320}$ (80×4)
      24
      $\underline{24}$ (6×4)
    Answer = 86

b $335 \div 5 \approx 70$ $5\overline{)335}$
      $\underline{300}$ (60×5)
      35
      $\underline{35}$ (7×5)
    Answer = 67

c $496 \div 8 \approx 60$ $8\overline{)496}$
      $\underline{480}$ (60×8)
      16
      $\underline{16}$ (2×8)
    Answer = 62

d $546 \div 6 \approx 90$ $6\overline{)564}$
      $\underline{540}$ (90×6)
      24
      $\underline{24}$ (4×6)
    Answer = 94

e $477 \div 9 \approx 50$ $9\overline{)477}$
      $\underline{450}$ (50×9)
      27
      $\underline{27}$ (3×9)
    Answer = 53

f $518 \div 7 \approx 70$ $7\overline{)518}$
      $\underline{490}$ (70×7)
      28
      $\underline{28}$ (4×7)
    Answer = 74

SCM 26

1 a £5 ≈ 30 Malaysian ringitts
   £10 ≈ 60 Malaysian ringitts
   £50 ≈ 300 Malaysian ringitts

b £5 ≈ 60 Danish Kroner
   £10 ≈ 120 Danish Kroner
   £25 ≈ 300 Danish Kroner

c £20 ≈ 240 Hong Kong dollars
   £50 ≈ 600 Hong Kong dollars
   £100 ≈ 1200 Hong Kong dollars

d £5 ≈ 12 Australian dollars
   £10 ≈ 27 Australian dollars
   £20 ≈ 48 Australian dollars

e £5 ≈ 310 Indian rupees
   £10 ≈ 620 Indian rupees
   £50 ≈ 3100 Indian rupees

2 a £139   **b** £68

SCM 27

1

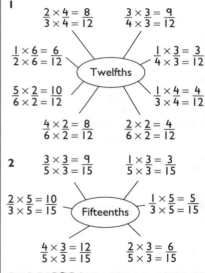

$$\frac{2 \times 4}{3 \times 4} = \frac{8}{12} \qquad \frac{3 \times 3}{4 \times 3} = \frac{9}{12}$$

$$\frac{1 \times 6}{2 \times 6} = \frac{6}{12} \qquad \frac{1 \times 3}{4 \times 3} = \frac{3}{12}$$

Twelfths

$$\frac{5 \times 2}{6 \times 2} = \frac{10}{12} \qquad \frac{1 \times 4}{3 \times 4} = \frac{4}{12}$$

$$\frac{4 \times 2}{6 \times 2} = \frac{8}{12} \qquad \frac{2 \times 2}{6 \times 2} = \frac{4}{12}$$

2
$$\frac{3 \times 3}{5 \times 3} = \frac{9}{15} \qquad \frac{1 \times 3}{5 \times 3} = \frac{3}{15}$$

$$\frac{2 \times 5}{3 \times 5} = \frac{10}{15} \qquad \frac{1 \times 5}{3 \times 5} = \frac{5}{15}$$

Fifteenths

$$\frac{4 \times 3}{5 \times 3} = \frac{12}{15} \qquad \frac{2 \times 3}{5 \times 3} = \frac{6}{15}$$

SCM 28

1 5 5.1 5.2 5.3 5.4 5.5 5.6 5.7 5.8 5.9 6

  a 5.4 is nearest to 5
  b 5.7 is nearest to 6
  c 5.1 is nearest to 5
  d 5.9 is nearest to 6

2 7 7.1 7.2 7.3 7.4 7.5 7.6 7.7 7.8 7.9 8

  a 7.8 is nearest to 8
  b 7.5 is nearest to 8

c 7.2 is nearest to 7
d 7.6 is nearest to 8

3 2.4 2.41 2.42 2.43 2.44 2.45 2.46 2.47 2.48 2.49 2.5

a 2.46 is nearest to 2.5
b 2.43 is nearest to 2.4
c 2.45 is nearest to 2.5
d 2.49 is nearest to 2.5

4 6.8 6.81 6.82 6.83 6.84 6.85 6.86 6.87 6.88 6.89 6.9

a 6.81 is nearest to 6.8
b 6.85 is nearest to 6.9
c 6.88 is nearest to 6.9
d 6.82 is nearest to 6.8

5 9.2 9.21 9.22 9.23 9.24 9.25 9.26 9.27 9.28 9.29 9.3

a 9.24 is nearest to 9.2
b 9.26 is nearest to 9.3
c 9.21 is nearest to 9.2
d 9.29 is nearest to 9.3

SCM 29
Open

SCM 30
a Angle $a = 30°$
Angle a is acute
b Angle $b = 60°$
Angle b is acute
c Angle $c = 90°$
Angle c is a right angle
d Angle $d = 120°$
Angle d is obtuse
e Angle $e = 60°$
Angle e is acute
f Angle $f = 30°$
Angle f is acute

SCM 31
Open

SCM 32
1 1 Area $= 9\,cm^2$ 2 Area $= 8\,cm^2$
3 Area $= 12\,cm^2$ 4 Area $= 15\,cm^2$
5 Area $= 16\,cm^2$ 6 Area $= 20\,cm^2$

2

Rectangles	Area of shape
1 and 3	$9\,cm^2 + 12\,cm^2 = 21\,cm^2$
2 and 4	$8\,cm^2 + 15\,cm^2 = 23\,cm^2$
3 and 6	$12\,cm^2 + 20\,cm^2 = 32\,cm^2$
4 and 5	$15\,cm^2 + 16\,cm^2 = 31\,cm^2$
5 and 1	$16\,cm^2 + 9\,cm^2 = 25\,cm^2$
6 and 4	$20\,cm^2 + 15\,cm^2 = 35\,cm^2$
2 and 6	$8\,cm^2 + 20\,cm^2 = 28\,cm^2$
3 and 4	$12\,cm^2 + 15\,cm^2 = 27\,cm^2$

SCM 33
1

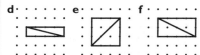

area $= 6\,cm^2$ area $= 3\,cm^2$ area $= 2\,cm^2$

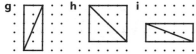

area $= 2\,cm^2$ area $= 4.5\,cm^2$ area $= 4\,cm^2$

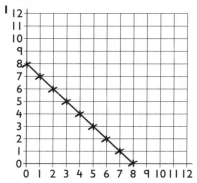

area $= 5\,cm^2$ area $= 8\,cm^2$ area $= 5\,cm^2$

SCM 34
1

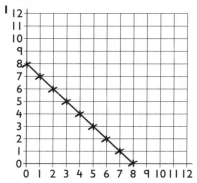

Collins Primary Maths

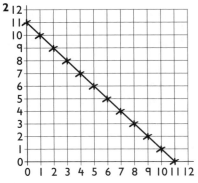

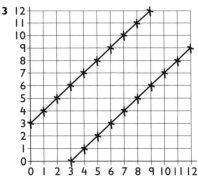

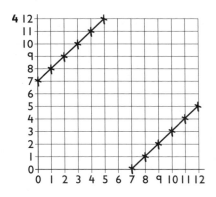

SCM 35

a	251	b	725	c	861
	+ 596		+ 169		+ 582
	847		921		1443

d	384	e	684	f	745
	+ 430		+ 284		+ 684
	814		968		1429

g	507	h	749	i	542
	+ 326		+ 218		+ 961
	833		967		1503

j	419	k	486	l	842
	+ 458		+ 395		+ 395
	877		881		1237

m	486	n	281	o	206
	+ 309		+ 973		+ 599
	795		1254		805

p	672	q	366	r	467
	+ 285		+ 518		+ 628
	957		884		1095

SCM 36

1 a $37 + 42 = 79$
$30 + 40 = 70$
$7 + 2 = 9$

b $51 + 26 = 77$
$50 + 20 = 70$
$1 + 6 = 7$

c $34 + 68 = 102$
$30 + 60 = 90$
$4 + 8 = 12$

d $49 + 65 = 114$
$40 + 60 = 100$
$9 + 5 = 14$

e $76 + 35 = 111$
$70 + 30 = 100$
$6 + 5 = 11$

f $87 + 59 = 146$
$80 + 50 = 130$
$7 + 9 = 16$

2 a $83 - 45 = 38$
$83 - 40 = 43$
$43 - 5 = 38$

b $96 - 62 = 34$
$96 - 60 = 36$
$36 - 2 = 34$

c $75 - 49 = 26$
$75 - 40 = 35$
$35 - 9 = 26$

d $87 - 53 = 34$
$87 - 50 = 37$
$37 - 3 = 34$

e $63 - 37 = 26$
$63 - 30 = 33$
$33 - 7 = 26$

f $98 - 27 = 71$
$98 - 20 = 78$
$78 - 7 = 71$

SCM 37
Open

SCM 38
1 a 0.6   **b** 0.3   **c** 0.9   **d** 0.8   **e** 0.4
2 a 0.9   **b** 1.7   **c** 2.8   **d** 3   **e** 3.8

SCM 39
  a 4, 6, 10, 14, 16, 18, 20
  b 10, 15, 20, 25, 30, 40, 45
  c 6, 9, 15, 18, 24, 27, 30
  d 8, 16, 20, 24, 28, 32, 36
  e 32, 40, 48, 56, 64, 72, 80
  f 36, 45, 54, 63, 72, 81, 90
  g 12, 18, 24, 30, 42, 48, 54
  h 30, 40, 50, 60, 70, 80, 90
  i 28, 35, 42, 49, 56, 63, 70

Collins Primary Maths

Answers

Support Copymasters

SCM 40

1 a $15 \times 10 = 150$
 b $38 \times 10 = 380$
 c $68 \times 10 = 680$
 d $713 \times 10 = 7130$
 e $601 \times 10 = 6010$
 f $9631 \times 10 = 96310$
2 a $35 \times 100 = 3500$
 b $45 \times 100 = 4500$
 c $75 \times 100 = 7500$
 d $381 \times 100 = 38100$
 e $496 \times 100 = 49600$
 f $843 \times 100 = 84300$
3 a $650 \div 10 = 65$
 b $350 \div 10 = 35$
 c $680 \div 10 = 68$
 d $6000 \div 10 = 600$
 e $52130 \div 10 = 5213$
 f $64520 \div 10 = 6452$
4 a $500 \div 100 = 5$
 b $4200 \div 100 = 42$
 c $6100 \div 100 = 61$
 d $61300 \div 100 = 613$
 e $7520 \div 100 = 75.2$
 f $3940 \div 100 = 39.4$

SCM 41

 a ($\approx 230 \times 15 = 3450$) $232 \times 14 = 3248$
 b ($\approx 350 \times 10 = 3500$) $351 \times 12 = 4212$
 c ($\approx 150 \times 25 = 3750$) $146 \times 23 = 3358$
 d ($\approx 240 \times 25 = 6000$) $237 \times 25 = 5925$
 e ($\approx 250 \times 14 = 3500$) $256 \times 14 = 3584$
 f ($\approx 350 \times 25 = 8750$) $352 \times 26 = 9152$

SCM 42

1 a $142 \times 25 \approx 140 \times 25 = 3500$
 b $321 \times 13 \approx 320 \times 12 = 3840$
 c $284 \times 22 \approx 285 \times 20 = 5700$
 d $197 \times 14 \approx 200 \times 15 = 3000$
 e $247 \times 22 \approx 250 \times 22 = 5500$
 f $313 \times 26 \approx 315 \times 25 = 7875$
 g $252 \times 32 \approx 250 \times 30 = 7500$

 h $324 \times 15 \approx 320 \times 15 = 4800$
2 a $142 \times 25 = 3550$
 b $321 \times 13 = 4173$
 c $284 \times 22 = 6248$
 d $197 \times 14 = 2758$
 e $247 \times 22 = 5434$
 f $313 \times 26 = 8138$
 g $252 \times 32 = 8064$
 h $324 \times 15 = 4860$

SCM 43

 a $594 \div 22 \approx 600 \div 20 = 30$
  $594 \div 22 = 27$
 b $312 \div 12 \approx 300 \div 12 = 25$
  $312 \div 12 = 26$
 c $375 \div 15 \approx 360 \div 15 = 24$
  $375 \div 15 = 25$
 d $418 \div 19 \approx 420 \div 20 = 21$
  $418 \div 19 = 22$
 e $693 \div 21 \approx 700 \div 20 = 35$
  $693 \div 21 = 33$
 f $768 \div 24 \approx 775 \div 25 = 31$
  $768 \div 24 = 32$

SCM 44

 a $528 \div 12 \approx 540 \div 12 = 45$
  $528 \div 12 = 44$
 b $672 \div 21 \approx 680 \div 20 = 34$
  $672 \div 21 = 32$
 c $540 \div 15 \approx 555 \div 15 = 37$
  $540 \div 15 = 36$
 d $286 \div 13 \approx 300 \div 12 = 25$
  $286 \div 13 = 22$
 e $682 \div 22 \approx 680 \div 20 = 34$
  $682 \div 22 = 31$
 f $528 \div 24 \approx 525 \div 25 = 21$
  $528 \div 24 = 22$

SCM 45

 a $\frac{3}{4} = \frac{9}{12}$ $\frac{2}{3} = \frac{8}{12}$ Larger fraction: $\frac{9}{12}$
  Smaller fraction: $\frac{8}{12}$

b $\frac{1}{3} = \frac{5}{15}$ $\frac{2}{5} = \frac{6}{15}$ Larger fraction: $\frac{6}{15}$
Smaller fraction: $\frac{5}{15}$
c $\frac{1}{2} = \frac{3}{6}$ $\frac{1}{3} = \frac{2}{6}$ Larger fraction: $\frac{3}{6}$
Smaller fraction: $\frac{2}{6}$
d $\frac{4}{5} = \frac{12}{15}$ $\frac{2}{3} = \frac{10}{15}$ Larger fraction: $\frac{12}{15}$
Smaller fraction: $\frac{10}{15}$
e $\frac{4}{6} = \frac{12}{18}$ $\frac{7}{9} = \frac{14}{18}$ Larger fraction: $\frac{14}{18}$
Smaller fraction: $\frac{12}{18}$
f $\frac{2}{3} = \frac{16}{24}$ $\frac{7}{8} = \frac{21}{24}$ Larger fraction: $\frac{21}{24}$
Smaller fraction: $\frac{16}{24}$

SCM 46

a $\frac{3}{5}$: $1 \div 5 = 0.2$ $\quad 0.2 \times 3 = 0.6$
b $\frac{2}{10}$: $1 \div 10 = 0.1$ $\quad 0.1 \times 2 = 0.2$
c $\frac{5}{8}$: $1 \div 8 = 0.125$ $\quad 0.125 \times 5 = 0.625$
d $\frac{7}{20}$: $1 \div 20 = 0.05$ $\quad 0.05 \times 7 = 0.35$
e $\frac{16}{25}$: $1 \div 25 = 0.04$ $\quad 0.04 \times 16 = 0.64$
f $\frac{8}{10}$: $1 \div 10 = 0.1$ $\quad 0.1 \times 8 = 0.8$
g $\frac{3}{8}$: $1 \div 8 = 0.125$ $\quad 0.125 \times 3 = 0.375$
h $\frac{18}{20}$: $1 \div 20 = 0.05$ $\quad 0.05 \times 18 = 0.9$
i $\frac{4}{5}$: $1 \div 5 = 0.2$ $\quad 0.2 \times 4 = 0.8$
j $\frac{7}{25}$: $1 \div 25 = 0.04$ $\quad 0.04 \times 7 = 0.28$

SCM 47

1 a

$\frac{1}{2}$

b
12½%

c
$\frac{1}{10}$

d
$\frac{1}{5}$

e
0.25
0 ——— 1
0.25

f
$\frac{1}{8}$

g

25%

h
0.1
0 ——— 1
0.1

i

20%

j

75%

k
0.2
0 ——— 1
0.2

l
$\frac{1}{4}$

m
0.75
0 ——— 1
0.75

n
0.125
0 ——— 1
0.125

o
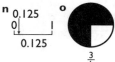
$\frac{3}{4}$

p

50%

q
0.5
0 ——— 1
0.5

r

10%

2 a $\frac{1}{2} = 50\% = 0.5$
b $\frac{1}{4} = 25\% = 0.25$
c $\frac{1}{5} = 20\% = 0.2$
d $\frac{1}{10} = 10\% = 0.1$
e $\frac{1}{8} = 12\frac{1}{2}\% = 0.125$
f $\frac{3}{4} = 75\% = 0.75$

SCM 48

1

Eggs	Flour
2	100 g
4	200 g
6	300 g
8	400 g
10	500 g
12	600 g
14	700 g
16	800 g

a 500 g
b 16

2

Orange	Water
1	4
2	8
3	12
4	16
5	20
6	24
7	28
8	32

a 4 parts of water
b 24 parts of water

SCM 49

1 a $\frac{3}{9} = \frac{1}{3}$ **b** $\frac{4}{20} = \frac{1}{5}$ **c** $\frac{6}{12} = \frac{1}{2}$
d $\frac{8}{12} = \frac{2}{3}$ **e** $\frac{25}{30} = \frac{5}{6}$ **f** $\frac{10}{16} = \frac{5}{8}$
g $\frac{14}{49} = \frac{2}{7}$ **h** $\frac{24}{40} = \frac{3}{5}$ **i** $\frac{21}{27} = \frac{7}{9}$

Collins Primary Maths

2 a $\frac{3}{6}=\frac{1}{2}$ b $\frac{2}{10}=\frac{1}{5}$ c $\frac{5}{25}=\frac{1}{5}$
  d $\frac{4}{20}=\frac{1}{5}$ e $\frac{9}{12}=\frac{3}{4}$ f $\frac{16}{20}=\frac{4}{5}$
  g $\frac{15}{18}=\frac{5}{6}$ h $\frac{20}{32}=\frac{5}{8}$
3 a $\frac{1}{4}=\frac{3}{12}$ b $\frac{1}{6}=\frac{5}{30}$ c $\frac{1}{2}=\frac{8}{16}$
  d $\frac{7}{21}=\frac{1}{3}$ e $\frac{4}{20}=\frac{1}{5}$ f $\frac{4}{32}=\frac{1}{8}$
  g $\frac{3}{5}=\frac{12}{20}$ h $\frac{4}{7}=\frac{8}{14}$ i $\frac{2}{3}=\frac{16}{24}$
  j $\frac{12}{16}=\frac{3}{4}$ k $\frac{9}{21}=\frac{3}{7}$ l $\frac{18}{48}=\frac{3}{8}$

SCM 50
1 a £9 b £3 c £3 d £5 e £20
  f £40 g £7 h £9 i £7
2 a £6, £12, £18
  b £8, £16, £24, £32
  c £5, £10, £20, £25
3 a £9 b £6 c £8 d £10 e £24
  f £6 g £42 h £25 i £60 j £60
  k £450 l £28

SCM 51
1
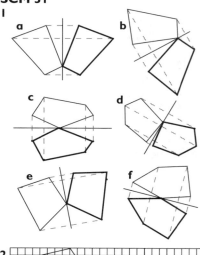
2
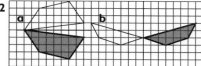

SCM 52
1

Shape	Number seen in mirrors	Drawing
square	3	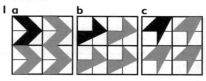
rectangle	3	
equilateral triangle	5	
regular hexagon	2	
parallelogram	2	
rhombus	2	

2 Parallelogram

SCM 53
1 a   b   c
2 Open

SCM 54

SCM 55
Open

SCM 56
1 a 200 ml b 220 ml c 460 ml
  d 280 ml e 700 ml f 160 ml
2 a 30 cl b 60 cl c 12 cl

SCM 57

1 $5 + 5 = 10$	**2** $7 + 8 = 15$
3 $9 + 9 = 18$	**4** $8 + 4 = 12$
5 $5 + 3 = 8$	**6** $9 + 2 = 11$
7 $9 + 8 = 17$	**8** $5 + 6 = 11$
9 $8 + 5 + 13$	**10** $9 + 1 = 10$
11 $9 + 6 = 15$	**12** $6 + 8 = 14$
13 $13 + 4 = 17$	**14** $3 + 4 = 7$
15 $14 + 6 = 20$	**16** $6 + 4 = 10$
17 $10 + 9 = 19$	**18** $12 + 6 = 18$
19 $2 + 13 = 15$	**20** $6 + 6 = 12$
21 $5 + 4 = 9$	**22** $7 + 3 = 10$
23 $8 + 8 = 16$	**24** $10 + 5 = 15$
25 $11 + 8 = 19$	**26** $11 + 1 = 12$
27 $14 + 1 = 15$	**28** $12 + 5 = 17$
29 $9 + 7 = 16$	**30** $18 + 0 = 18$

SCM 58

1 2467	**2** 39
3 £10.14	**4** 126 hours

SCM 59

a 0.2	b 0.5	c 0.25	d 0.1
0.4	1.0	0.50	0.2
0.6	1.5	0.75	0.3
0.8	2.0	1.00	0.4
1.0	2.5	1.25	0.5
1.2	3.0	1.50	0.6
1.4	3.5	1.75	0.7
1.6	4.0	2.00	0.8
1.8	4.5	2.25	0.9
2.0	5.0	2.50	1.0
2.2	5.5	2.75	1.1
2.4	6.0	3.00	1.2
2.6	6.5	3.25	1.3
2.8	7.0	3.50	1.4
3.0	7.5	3.75	1.5
3.2	8.0	4.00	1.6
3.4	8.5	4.25	1.7
3.6	9.0	4.50	1.8
3.8	9.5	4.75	1.9
4.0	10.0	5.00	2.0

SCM 60

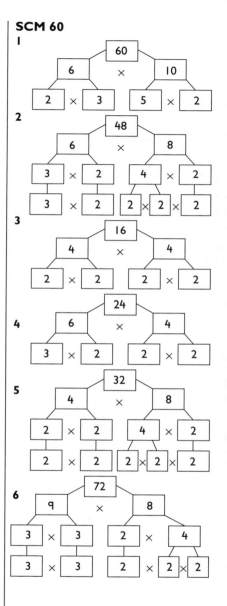

Collins Primary Maths

7

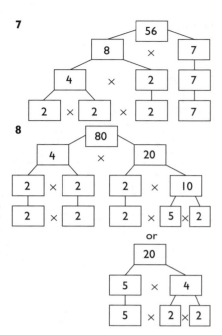

```
              56
        8    ×    7
     4   ×   2    7
   2 × 2  ×  2    7
```

8

```
            80
     4      ×      20
  2 × 2        2  ×  10
  2 × 2        2  ×  5 × 2
```

or

```
         20
     5   ×   4
     5   ×  2 × 2
```

.

Extension Copymasters

Autumn Term

ECM 1
Answers will vary
As the negative number decreases the positive number increases.

ECM 2
Open

ECM 3

35×26

D	H
~~35~~	~~26~~
70	13
~~140~~	~~6~~
280	3
560	1
910	

27×46

D	H
~~27~~	~~46~~
54	23
108	11
216	5
~~432~~	~~2~~
864	1
1242	

72×36

D	H
~~72~~	~~36~~
~~144~~	~~18~~
288	9
~~576~~	~~4~~
~~1152~~	~~2~~
2304	1
2592	

52×38

D	H
~~52~~	~~38~~
104	19
208	9
~~416~~	~~4~~
~~832~~	~~2~~
1664	1
1976	

23×34

D	H
~~23~~	~~34~~
46	17
~~92~~	~~8~~
~~184~~	~~4~~
~~368~~	~~2~~
736	1
782	

44×29

D	H
44	29
~~88~~	~~14~~
176	7
352	3
704	1
1276	

48×36

D	H
~~48~~	~~36~~
~~96~~	~~18~~
192	9
~~384~~	~~4~~
~~768~~	~~2~~
1536	1
1728	

82×28

D	H
~~82~~	~~28~~
~~164~~	~~14~~
328	7
656	3
1312	1
2296	

56×74

D	H
~~56~~	~~74~~
112	37
~~224~~	~~18~~
448	9
~~896~~	~~4~~
~~1792~~	~~2~~
3584	1
4144	

Collins Primary Maths

ECM 4

1 a

$$\begin{array}{c|cccc} \times & 7000 & 100 & 20 & 4 \\ \hline 3 & 21000 & 300 & 60 & 12 \end{array} = 21372$$

$7\boxed{1}\ 24 \times 3$

b $3426 \times 6 = 20\,556$

c $4583 \times 7 = 32\,081$

d $1679 \times 9 = 15\,111$

e $2538 \times 8 = 20\,304$

f $5103 \times 5 = 25\,515$

g $9245 \times 2 = 18\,490$

h $6410 \times 3 = 19\,230$

ECM 5

Answers will vary

ECM 6

Answers will vary

a $\frac{1}{2} = \frac{5}{10} = \frac{7}{14} = \frac{9}{18} = \frac{11}{22} = \frac{15}{30} = \frac{25}{50}$

b $\frac{2}{3} = \frac{4}{6} = \frac{10}{15} = \frac{14}{21} = \frac{16}{24} = \frac{26}{39} = \frac{28}{42}$

c $\frac{1}{4} = \frac{3}{12} = \frac{5}{20} = \frac{7}{28} = \frac{9}{36} = \frac{11}{44} = \frac{13}{52}$

d $\frac{1}{3} = \frac{3}{9} = \frac{5}{15} = \frac{7}{21} = \frac{9}{27} = \frac{13}{39} = \frac{16}{48}$

e $\frac{3}{4} = \frac{6}{8} = \frac{9}{12} = \frac{21}{28} = \frac{27}{36} = \frac{33}{44} = \frac{36}{48}$

f $\frac{1}{5} = \frac{2}{10} = \frac{3}{15} = \frac{5}{25} = \frac{7}{35} = \frac{8}{40} = \frac{9}{45}$

g $\frac{1}{6} = \frac{2}{12} = \frac{4}{24} = \frac{5}{30} = \frac{7}{42} = \frac{9}{54} = \frac{11}{66}$

h $\frac{1}{7} = \frac{2}{14} = \frac{3}{21} = \frac{4}{28} = \frac{6}{42} = \frac{7}{49} = \frac{8}{56}$

i $\frac{1}{8} = \frac{2}{16} = \frac{4}{32} = \frac{5}{40} = \frac{7}{56} = \frac{9}{72} = \frac{10}{80}$

j $\frac{1}{10} = \frac{2}{20} = \frac{4}{40} = \frac{7}{70} = \frac{10}{100} = \frac{11}{110} = \frac{13}{130}$

k $\frac{1}{12} = \frac{2}{24} = \frac{4}{48} = \frac{6}{72} = \frac{7}{84} = \frac{10}{120} = \frac{11}{132}$

l $\frac{4}{7} = \frac{8}{14} = \frac{12}{21} = \frac{24}{42} = \frac{28}{49} = \frac{36}{63} = \frac{44}{77}$

ECM 7

a $\frac{3}{5} = 0.6$ **b** $\frac{2}{8} = 0.25$

c $\frac{3}{2} = 1.5$ **d** $\frac{9}{12} = 0.75$

e $\frac{7}{4} = 1.75$ **f** $\frac{3}{6} = 0.5$

g $\frac{2}{8} = 0.25$ **h** $\frac{5}{10} = 0.5$

i $\frac{11}{4} = 2.75$ **j** $\frac{5}{8} = 0.625$

ECM 8

Videos: £10.80   DVDs: £18.90

CDs: £9   CD rack: £17.55

T-shirts: £4.95

Answers will vary

ECM 9

Answers will vary

ECM 10

2 a $\frac{1}{4}$ **b** 10

3 Answers will vary

4 a $\frac{1}{2}$, 30   **b** $\frac{1}{6}$

ECM 11

1 a 5   **b** 30

c £4.925, rounded to £4.93

d 202.5 g

2 a 3 g   **b** 60 cm

ECM 12

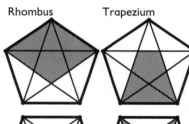

Rhombus   Trapezium

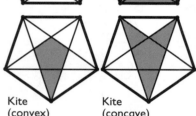

Kite   Kite
(convex)   (concave)

ECM 13

Open

ECM 14

1, 2 and 4

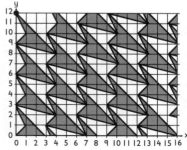

3

Shape	Corresponding vertices	
	x-co-ordinate	y-co-ordinate
1	0	12
2	3	10
3	6	8
4	9	6
5	12	4
6	15	2

ECM 15
Open

ECM 16
1 4, 10, 22, 28

2, 3
Number of steps	Perimeter outline	Difference
1	4	
2	10	6
3	16	6
4	22	6
5	28	6
6	34	6

4 Perimeter of the outline increases by 6 units each time, so perimeter is $6 \times$ number of steps $- 2$.

5 a 58   b 148   c $6n - 2$

ECM 17
1 Open

2
Number of pins on the perimeter	4	5	6	7	8
Area of shape	1	$1\frac{1}{2}$	2	$2\frac{1}{2}$	3

3 a 4 square units   b 5 square units

ECM 18
1 $9004 - 4996 = 4008$
2 $8006 - 5992 = 2014$
3 $7001 - 3977 = 3024$
4 $5009 - 1985 = 3024$
5 $6012 - 2999 = 3013$
6 $497 + 195 = 692$
7 $862 + 297 = 1159$
8 $871 - 301 = 570$
9 $1867 - 803 = 2670$
10 $2965 + 1498 = 4463$
11 $7.3 + 2.1 = 9.4$
12 $2.6 - 0.9 = 1.7$
13 $8.4 + 5.1 = 13.5$
14 $9.7 - 4.9 = 4.8$
15 $5.6 + 7.1 = 12.7$
16 $867 + 942 = 1809$
17 $733 + 621 = 1354$
18 $584 + 978 = 1562$
19 $652 + 834 = 1486$
20 $761 + 758 = 1519$

ECM 19
Answers may vary from those given below.

a $241 + 356 = 597$
b $154 + 632 = 786$
c $615 + 234 = 849$
d $542 + 163 = 705$
e $536 + 142 = 678$
f $654 + 321 = 975$
g $123 + 654 = 777$
h $316 + 542 = 858$
i $265 + 341 = 606$

ECM 20
1 a 1 and 50   b 1 and 100
  c The difference between consecutive triangular numbers increases by 1 to give the sequence of natural numbers, starting at 3. So, the frequency of triangular numbers is greatest for low values of the differences.

2 a 3, 6, 10, 15, 21, 28, 36, 45, 55, 66, 78, 91, 105
  b See 1 c

3 36 and 45
  105 and 120
  190 and 210

Collins Primary Maths

ECM 21

1 **1** A = 25 (25 + 25 = 50)
  2 B = 15 (60 − 15 − 15 − 15 −15 = 0)
  3 C = 3 (3 × 3 × 3 = 27)
  4 D = 11 (11 + 11 + 11 + 11 = 44)
  5 E = 10 (10 × 10 = 90 + 10)
  6 F = 12, G = 6 (12 + 12 + 12 = 6 × 6)
  7 H = 8 (8 × 9 = 80 − 8)
  8 J = 7 (7 × 7 + 7 = 56)
  9 K = 50 (100 − 50 = 50)
10 L = 1 (1 ÷ 1 × 10 = 10)

2 a 23 + 69 = 92   **b** 23 × 9 = 207
  c 93 + 26 = 119   **d** 632 × 9 = 5688
  e 369 ÷ 9 = 41   **f** 96 − 32 = 64
  g 69 ÷ 3 = 23   **h** 62 × 9 = 558
  i 632 − 9 = 623   **j** 36 ÷ 2 = 18
  k 936 ÷ 2 = 468   **l** 236 + 9 = 245

Extension Copymasters

ECM 22

1 a £4.70   **b** £47   **c** £470
   d £47 000   **e** £423

2 a 32 000   **b** 320   **c** £1.20
   d £1200   **e** £120 000

ECM 23

1 Times table or number facts grid up to 10×10.

ECM 24

a

162	
6	27

2	3	9

b

224	
8	28

2	4	7

c

288	
8	36

2	4	9

d

324	
9	36

3	3	12

e

384	
8	48

1	8	6

f

675	
9	75

3	3	25

g

512	
8	64

2	4	16

h

648	
9	72

1	9	8

i

735	
7	105

1	7	15

j

864	
12	72

2	6	12

1	2	3	4

k

4000	
50	80

5	10	8

1	5	2	4

l

1250	
25	50

5	5	10

5	1	5	2

ECM 25

1 Calculations b, e and f will not have a remainder.

   a $678 \div 9 \approx 700 \div 10 = 70$

$$9\overline{)678}$$
$$\underline{-630} \quad (70 \times 9)$$
$$48$$
$$\underline{-45} \quad (5 \times 9)$$
$$3$$

Answer 75 r3

$$9\overline{)678}^{\,75\ r3}$$
$$\underline{-63}$$
$$48$$
$$\underline{-45}$$
$$3$$

b $372 \div 4 \approx 360 \div 4 = 90$
    $372 \div 4 = 93$

c $736 \div 3 \approx 750 \div 3 = 250$
    $736 \div 3 = 245\ r1$

d $526 \div 4 \approx 540 \div 4 = 135$
    $526 \div 4 = 131\ r2$

e $747 \div 9 \approx 720 \div 9 = 80$
    $747 \div 9 = 83$

f $561 \div 3 \approx 540 \div 3 = 180$
    $561 \div 3 = 187$

ECM 26

Answers will vary

ECM 27

a $\frac{12}{30}, \frac{15}{30}, \frac{12}{30}, \frac{6}{30}, \frac{10}{30}$

b $\frac{4}{20}, \frac{16}{20}, \frac{15}{20}, \frac{16}{20}, \frac{18}{20}$

c $\frac{50}{80}, \frac{16}{80}, \frac{8}{80}, \frac{20}{80}, \frac{48}{80}$

d $\frac{28}{40}, \frac{32}{40}, \frac{28}{40}, \frac{30}{40}, \frac{5}{40}$

e $\frac{15}{40}, \frac{8}{40}, \frac{8}{40}, \frac{32}{40}, \frac{4}{40}$

f $\frac{36}{40}, \frac{5}{40}, \frac{24}{40}, \frac{40}{40}, \frac{36}{40}$

ECM 28

2 a £9.20   **b** 117
   c 1975   **d** £83.42
   e 201.5   **f** £18.49
   g 1.5   **h** £406.70
   i £12.60   **j** 3600

ECM 29

Open

ECM 30

1 a

angle	A	B	C	D	E	F
degrees	72°	72°	54°	54°	72°	72°

b The angles subtended at the centre of a pentagon by its sides are equal, each being $360° \div 5 = 72°$, as found for A and B. The exterior angles are also equal, each being $360° \div 5 = 72°$, as found for E and F. Angle C = Angle D = $(180° - 72°) \div 2 = 54°$.

Collins Primary Maths

2 a

angle	K	L	M	N	O	P	Q
degrees	36°	72°	36°	36°	36°	72°	36°

b angle (K + L) = 108°
angle (M + N + O) = 108°

c The interior angles of a regular pentagon are all equal to 108°.

3 a

angle	X	Y	Z
degrees	108°	108°	108°

b

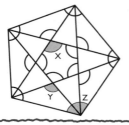

ECM 31

1

	Number of sides	Frequency	Sum or degrees at vertex
a	3	6	6 × 60° = 360°
b	4	4	4 × 90° = 360°
c	6	3	3 × 120° = 360°

2 a (2 × 90°) + (3 × 60°) = 360°
b (2 × 90°) + (3 × 60°) = 360°
c 120° + 60° + (2 × 90°) = 360°
d 120° + (4 × 60°) = 360°
e 120° + (2 × 90°) + 60° = 360°
f 90° + (2 × 135°) = 360°
g 60° + (2 × 150°) = 360°

ECM 32

1

shape	A	B	C	D	E
area in cm²	16	16	40	32	40

2

Area of the triangle = 72 cm²

3

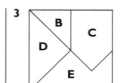

Area of square = 128 cm²

4

Area of the square = 144 cm²

ECM 33

1 a 5 square units
b 8 square units
c 13 square units

2

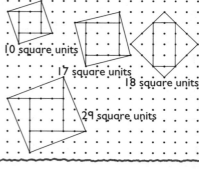

10 square units

17 square units

18 square units

29 square units

ECM 34

1 28.4 ml

2

(fl oz)	(ml)
0	0
4	110
8	230
12	340
16	450
20	570

3 Fluid ounces and millilitres conversion graph

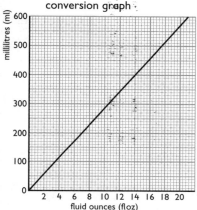

4 a 170 ml   **b** 370 ml
  c 480 ml   **d** 70 ml

5 a 8.8 fl oz   **b** 3.2 fl oz
  c 22.5 fl oz   **d** 13.4 fl oz

ECM 35

a	48 632	**b**	67 849	**c**	51 962		
	+ 31 270		+ 5772		+ 45 173		
	79 902		73 621		97 135		

d	48 609	**e**	23 586	**f**	37 963
	+ 30 664		+ 27 043		+ 48 354
	79 273		50 629		86 317

g	76 219	**h**	81 219	**i**	27 924
	+ 80 106		+ 352 956		+ 181 458
	156 325		434 175		209 382

j   73 964
    + 74 543
    148 507

ECM 36

a	96 872	**b**	78 621	**c**	54 861
	− 37 485		− 39 411		− 50 883
	59 387		39 210		3978

d	681 427	**e**	721 604	**f**	400 782
	− 594 028		− 561 838		− 124 438
	87 399		159 766		276 344

g	952 631	**h**	581 046	**i**	773 652
	− 862 210		− 521 125		− 725 761
	90 421		59 921		47 891

j   997 684
    − 926 987
    70 697

ECM 37

a $0.26 + 0.3 = 0.56$
b $0.4 + 0.58 = 0.98$
c $0.75 + 0.6 = 1.35$
d $0.94 + 0.9 = 1.84$
e $0.2 + 0.51 = 0.71$
f $0.362 + 0.1 = 0.462$
g $0.5 + 0.264 = 0.764$
h $0.26 + 0.214 = 0.474$
i $0.6 + 0.301 = 0.901$
j $0.255 + 0.87 = 1.125$
k $0.9 - 0.57 = 0.33$
l $0.48 - 0.3 = 0.18$
m $0.7 - 0.21 = 0.49$
n $0.88 - 0.1 = 0.78$
o $0.9 - 0.01 = 0.89$
p $0.7 - 0.31 = 0.39$
q $0.8 - 0.366 = 0.434$
r $0.842 - 0.5 = 0.342$
s $0.65 - 0.201 = 0.449$
t $0.9 - 0.255 = 0.645$

ECM 38

1 1111
2 16.8 cm
3 Yellow: 140, Blue: 28, Red: 84, Black: 28
4 2.8 cm, average daily growth = 2.5 cm

ECM 39

2 2, 3 5, 7, 11, 13, 17, 19, 23, 29, 31, 37, 41, 43, 47, 53, 59, 61, 67, 71, 73, 79, 83, 89, 91, 97
3 They are divisible only by themselves and 1.

Collins Primary Maths

Answers

Extension Copymasters
Summer Term

ECM 40
Answers will vary

ECM 41

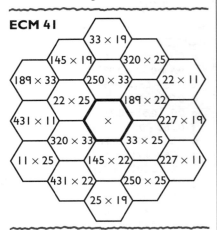

ECM 43
a $1196 \div 23 \approx 1200 \div 25 = 48$
$1196 \div 23 = 52$
b $1224 \div 34 \approx 1200 \div 30 = 40$
$1224 \div 34 = 36$
c $1849 \div 43 \approx 1800 \div 40 = 45$
$1849 \div 43 = 43$
d $1475 \div 25 \approx 1500 \div 25 = 60$
$1475 \div 25 = 59$
e $1352 \div 52 \approx 1400 \div 50 = 28$
$1352 \div 52 = 26$
f $1296 \div 36 \approx 1295 \div 35 = 37$
$1296 \div 36 = 36$
g $1392 \div 29 \approx 1500 \div 30 = 50$
$1392 \div 29 = 48$
h $1617 \div 33 \approx 1500 \div 30 = 50$
$1617 \div 33 = 49$

ECM 42

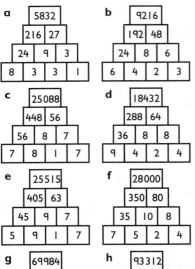

ECM 44
Shiblu
$56 \div 8 = 7$
$452 \times 8 = 3616$
$1288 \div 28 = 46$
$476 \div 17 = 17$
$37 \times 54 = 1998$
$486 \div 9 = 54$
$368 \times 42 = 15\,456$
$1102 \div 29 = 38$
$7 \times 6 = 42$

Thomas
$6 \times 9 = 54$
$1976 \div 52 = 38$
$298 \times 7 = 2086$
$945 \div 35 = 27$
$48 \times 9 = 432$
$368 \div 8 = 46$
$28 \times 47 = 1316$
$650 \div 26 = 25$

Shiblu passed 40 corners.
Thomas passed 45 corners.
Shiblu had the shortest journey.

ECM 45

a $\frac{4}{7} + \frac{3}{9} = \frac{36}{63} + \frac{21}{63} = \frac{57}{63} = 0.57 + 0.33 = 0.90$

b $\frac{2}{3} + \frac{4}{5} = \frac{10}{15} + \frac{12}{15} = \frac{22}{15}$ or $1\frac{7}{15} = 0.66 + 0.8 = 1.46$

c $\frac{2}{10} + \frac{6}{20} = \frac{4}{20} + \frac{6}{20} = \frac{10}{20}$ or $\frac{1}{2} = 0.2 + 0.3 = 0.5$

d $\frac{1}{8} + \frac{2}{5} = \frac{5}{40} + \frac{16}{40} = \frac{21}{40} = 0.125 + 0.4 = 0.53$

e $\frac{9}{14} + \frac{5}{7} = \frac{9}{14} + \frac{10}{14} = \frac{19}{14}$ or $1\frac{5}{14} = 0.64 + 0.71 = 1.35$

f $\frac{1}{6} + \frac{3}{4} = \frac{2}{12} + \frac{9}{12} = \frac{11}{12} = 0.17 + 0.75 = 0.92$

g $\frac{16}{21} + \frac{2}{6} = \frac{32}{42} + \frac{14}{42} = \frac{46}{42}$ or $1\frac{4}{42} = 0.76 + 0.33 = 1.09$

h $\frac{3}{8} + \frac{9}{12} = \frac{9}{24} + \frac{18}{24} = \frac{27}{24}$ or $1\frac{3}{24} = 0.375 + 0.75 = 1.13$

i $\frac{4}{6} + \frac{3}{7} = \frac{28}{42} + \frac{18}{42} = \frac{46}{42}$ or $1\frac{4}{42} = 0.66 + 0.43 = 1.09$

j $\frac{4}{5} + \frac{1}{4} = \frac{16}{20} + \frac{5}{20} = \frac{21}{20}$ or $1\frac{1}{20} = 0.8 + 0.25 = 1.05$

ECM 46

a $5.604 - 0.004 = 5.6$
$5.604 + 0.396 = 6$

b $7.012 - 0.012 = 7.0$
$7.012 - 0.012 = 7$

c $9.638 - 0.038 = 9.6$
$9.638 + 0.362 = 10$

d $5.449 - 0.049 = 5.4$
$5.449 - 0.449 = 5$

e $3.007 - 0.007 = 3.0$
$3.007 - 0.007 = 3$

f $8.275 + 0.025 = 8.3$
$8.275 - 0.275 = 8$

g $4.137 - 0.037 = 4.1$
$4.137 - 0.137 = 4$

h $2.551 + 0.049 = 2.6$
$2.551 + 0.449 = 3$

i $11.607 - 0.007 = 11.6$
$11.607 + 0.393 = 12$

j $15.443 - 0.043 = 15.4$
$15.443 - 0.443 = 15$

k $16.972 + 0.028 = 17.0$
$16.972 + 0.028 = 17$

l $12.116 - 0.016 = 12.1$
$12.116 - 0.116 = 12$

ECM 47

a	13.02	b	87.98	c	1
d	81.92	e	71.44	f	140.13
g	31.28	h	383.64	i	22.33
j	491.4	k	636	l	2060.64

ECM 48

1 a Jan   b Jan   c Jason
Answers will vary

2 Sue 75%   Theo 40%
Florence 90%   Emma 66%
Rosa 80%   Barnaby 70%
Florence got the highest per cent.

ECM 49

1

Ingredients	Calculation	Percentage
carrots	$200 \div 500 \times 100$	40%
onions	$150 \div 500 \times 100$	30%
water	$100 \div 500 \times 100$	20%
other	$50 \div 500 \times 100$	10%

2

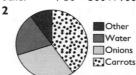

Other
Water
Onions
Carrots

3

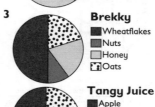

Brekky
Wheatflakes
Nuts
Honey
Oats

Tangy Juice
Apple
Pineapple
Grapefruit
Orange

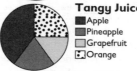

Crisbits
Other
Cheese
Rice
Potato

ECM 50

Answers will vary

ECM 51

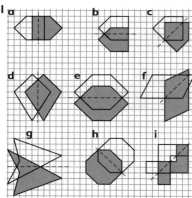

1

ECM 52

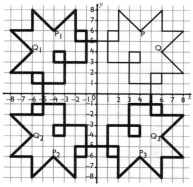

1

2

1st quadrant	2nd quadrant	3rd quadrant	4th quadrant
$P = (4, 6)$	$P_1 = (-4, 6)$	$P_2 = (-4, -6)$	$P_3 = (4, -6)$
$Q = (6, 4)$	$Q_1 = (-6, 4)$	$Q_2 = (-6, -4)$	$Q_3 = (6, -4)$

3 The size of each coordinate is unaltered by the reflections, but its sign changes according to the quadrant.

ECM 53

ECM 54

Open

ECM 55

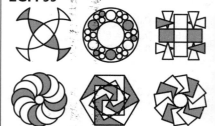

ECM 56

Open

ECM 57

	a		b		c	
		46.389		512.16		617.8
	+	72.614	+	385.9	+	933.86
		119.003		898.06		1551.66

	d		e		f	
		9.672		63.891		921.861
	+	3.999	+	45.206	+	47.3
		13.671		109.097		969.161

g	96.888	h	672.6	i	606.31
	+ 137.914		+ 301.17		+ 159.28
	234.802		973.77		765.59
j	78.962	k	963	l	9601.6
	+ 513.1		+ 578.7		+ 5804.97
	592.062		1541.7		15406.57
m	58412.7	n	901.9	o	764.6
	+ 9610.8		+ 529.33		+ 581.97
	68023.5		1431.23		1346.57

ECM 58

a $4800 + 2700 = 7500$
b $0.29 + 0.63 = 0.92$
c $27 + 96 = 123$
d $0.78 + 0.91 = 1.69$
e $4.9 + 5.6 = 10.5$
f $890 + 720 = 1610$
g $9100 + 8700 = 17\,800$
h $5.6 + 9.7 = 15.3$
i $94 + 72 = 166$
j $3800 + 1900 = 5700$
k $0.88 + 0.64 = 1.52$
l $6700 + 9900 = 16\,600$
m $7.3 + 4.9 = 12.2$
n $670 - 220 = 450$
o $4.9 - 2.7 = 2.2$
p $0.66 - 0.41 = 0.25$
q $8800 - 4900 = 3900$
r $93 - 47 = 46$
s $720 - 390 = 330$
t $5.8 - 3.9 = 1.9$
u $0.81 - 0.39 = 0.42$
v $9200 - 4800 = 4400$
w $680 - 190 = 490$
x $7.2 - 1.8 = 5.4$
y $87 - 33 = 54$
z $7100 - 4300 = 2800$

ECM 59

1   $7 \rightarrow 2 + 2 + 3$
  $9 \rightarrow 2 + 2 + 5$
  $11 \rightarrow 3 + 3 + 5$
  $13 \rightarrow 3 + 5 + 5$
   or $3 + 3 + 7$
  $15 \rightarrow 2 + 2 + 11$
  $17 \rightarrow 3 + 3 + 11$
   or $5 + 5 + 7$
   or $3 + 3 + 11$
  $19 \rightarrow 3 + 3 + 13$
   or $7 + 7 + 5$
  $21 \rightarrow 5 + 5 + 11$
  $23 \rightarrow 5 + 5 + 13$
  $25 \rightarrow 7 + 7 + 11$
   or $11 + 11 + 3$
  $27 \rightarrow 7 + 7 + 13$
   or $11 + 11 + 5$
  $29 \rightarrow 11 + 11 + 7$
   or $13 + 13 + 3$
  $31 \rightarrow 13 + 13 + 5$
   or $7 + 7 + 17$
  $33 \rightarrow 13 + 13 + 7$
   or $7 + 7 + 19$
  $35 \rightarrow 11 + 11 + 13$
  $37 \rightarrow 11 + 13 + 13$
   or $17 + 17 + 3$
  $39 \rightarrow 17 + 11 + 11$
   or $17 + 17 + 5$
  $41 \rightarrow 17 + 17 + 7$
   or $19 + 19 + 3$
  $43 \rightarrow 19 + 19 + 5$
  $45 \rightarrow 19 + 19 + 7$
   or $17 + 17 + 11$

2 The statement is true

ECM 60
Open

Homework Copymasters

Autumn Term

HCM 1
Refresher
1 a $40 \times 10 = 400$ **b** $10 \times 91 = 910$
   c $100 \times 80 = 8000$
2 a $510 \div 10 = 51$ **b** $9000 \div 100 = 90$
   c $2000 \div 10 = 200$

Practice
1 a $6.7 \times 10 = 67$
   b $1000 \times 55 = 55\,000$
   c $100 \times 1.2 = 120$
   d $2.5 \times 1000 = 2500$
2 a $71 \div 10 = 7.1$
   b $623 \div 100 = 6.23$
   c $7800 \div 10 = 780$
   d $8000 \div 100 = 80$
3 a $4.8 \times 100 = 480$
   b $90 \times 10 = 900$ and 0.9×1000
   c $4700 \div 1000 = 4.7$
   d $0.3 \div 10 = 0.03$

HCM 2
Refresher
Answers will vary

Practice

a

×	9	7	12	8
6	54	42	72	48
9	81	63	108	72
4	36	28	48	32
8	72	56	96	64
5	45	35	60	40
3	27	21	36	24
7	63	49	84	56

b

×	9	4	2	7	1	6	8
3	27	12	6	21	3	18	24
5	45	20	10	35	5	30	40
7	63	28	14	49	7	42	56

c

×	6	3	8	4	7
2	12	6	16	8	14
6	36	18	48	24	42
9	54	27	72	36	63
0	0	0	0	0	0

HCM 3
Refresher

$56 \times 2 = 112$	$78 \times 2 = 156$
$99 \times 2 = 198$	$37 \times 2 = 74$
$45 \times 2 = 90$	$96 \div 2 = 48$
$58 \div 2 = 29$	$34 \div 2 = 17$
$56 \div 2 = 28$	$94 \div 2 = 47$
$3.7 \times 2 = 7.4$	$10.2 \times 2 = 20.4$
$45.5 \times 2 = 91$	$18.4 \times 2 = 36.8$
$24 \times 2 = 48$	

Practice

$2600 \times 2 = 5200$	$930 \times 2 = 1860$
$0.52 \times 2 = 1.04$	$8800 \times 2 = 17\,600$
$650 \times 2 = 1300$	$0.36 \times 2 = 0.72$
$6900 \times 2 = 13\,800$	$9700 \times 2 = 19\,400$
$850 \times 2 = 1700$	$7500 \times 2 = 15\,000$
$8.6 \times 2 = 17.2$	$710 \times 2 = 1420$
$27.5 \times 2 = 55$	$3600 \times 2 = 7200$
$9800 \div 2 = 4900$	$26.4 \div 2 = 13.2$
$19\,100 \div 2 = 9550$	$1860 \div 2 = 930$
$15.2 \div 2 = 7.6$	$38.6 \div 2 = 19.3$
$17\,500 \div 2 = 8750$	$53 \div 2 = 26.5$
$1740 \div 2 = 870$	$82.4 \div 2 = 41.2$
$10\,500 \div 2 = 5250$	$890 \div 2 = 445$
$11\,800 \div 2 = 5900$	$13\,700 \div 2 = 6850$

HCM 4
Refresher
Answers will vary. Model answers:
   a 9000 **b** 9600 **c** $14\,000$
   d 5100 **e** $17\,000$ **f** $14\,400$
   g $51\,200$ **h** $65\,700$ **i** $41\,300$

Practice

a
$$2956 \times 3$$

(2000×3)	6000
(900×3)	2700
(50×3)	150
(6×3)	18
	8868

b $2362 \times 4 = 9448$

c $2783 \times 5 = 13\,915$

d $1638 \times 3 = 4914$

e $3425 \times 5 = 17\,125$

f $4772 \times 3 = 14\,316$

g $6358 \times 8 = 50\,864$

h $7264 \times 9 = 65\,376$

i $5936 \times 7 = 41\,552$

HCM 5
Refresher

a £99   b £44   c £168   d £282

Practice

a £624 + £846 + £360 = £1830

b £1125 − £1000 = £125 profit

c £1872 − £360 = £1512

d £98 + £180 + £575 = £853,
£1000 − £853 = £147 change

HCM 6
Refresher

$\frac{1}{2}$ is twice as much as $\frac{1}{4}$
$\frac{1}{4}$ is twice as much as $\frac{1}{8}$
$\frac{1}{2}$ is 4 times as much as $\frac{1}{8}$
$\frac{1}{3}$ is twice as much as $\frac{1}{6}$

Practice

$\frac{1}{2}$ is twice as much as $\frac{1}{4}$
$\frac{1}{2}$ is 4 times as much as $\frac{1}{8}$
$\frac{1}{2}$ is 6 times as much as $\frac{1}{12}$
$\frac{1}{2}$ is 7 times as much as $\frac{1}{14}$
$\frac{1}{2}$ is 8 times as much as $\frac{1}{16}$
$\frac{1}{2}$ is 10 times as much as $\frac{1}{20}$
$\frac{1}{2}$ is 5 times as much as $\frac{1}{10}$
$\frac{1}{8}$ is twice as much as $\frac{1}{16}$
$\frac{1}{10}$ is twice as much as $\frac{1}{20}$
$\frac{1}{4}$ is 4 times as much as $\frac{1}{16}$
$\frac{1}{4}$ is twice as much as $\frac{1}{8}$
$\frac{1}{4}$ is 5 times as much as $\frac{1}{20}$

HCM 7
Answers will vary

HCM 8
Answers will vary

HCM 9
Answers will vary

HCM 10
Refresher

Length (minutes)	Tally	Total
1–10	ЖН III	8
11–20	III	3
21–30	ЖН ЖН ЖН	15
31–40	ЖН I	7
41–50	ЖН	5
51–60	I	2

Practice

1

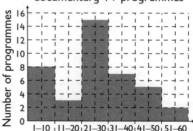

Length of news and documentary TV programmes

2a 21–30   b 11   c 7

HCM 11
Refresher

1a 5   b 18   c 50
2a 5   b 7   c 20
3a 3   b 5   c 20

Practice

1a 10   b 13   c 4   d 5
2a 2.5g b 150g c 28g
3a 61   b 54   c 70
4a £7.20 b £4.44

Collins Primary Maths

HCM 12
Refresher and Practice

1

a convex kite

b trapezium

c parallelogram

d concave kite

Practice

2

trapezium

trapezium

kite

parallelogram

quadrilateral

parallelogram

square

rectangle

square

square

HCM 13
Refresher and Practice

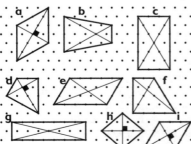

Practice

1 a: rhombus   d: kite
   h: rhombus   i: rhombus
2 g: rectangle

HCM 14
Open

HCM 15
Refresher and Practice

a

midpoint line = <u>3.9</u>cm
parallel side = <u>7.7</u>cm

b

midpoint line = <u>0.9</u>cm
parallel side = <u>1.8</u>cm

c

midpoint line = <u>3.8</u>cm
parallel side = <u>7.6</u>cm

d

midpoint line = <u>2.1</u>cm
parallel side = <u>4.2</u>cm

e

midpoint line = <u>1.6</u>cm
parallel side = <u>3.2</u>cm

f

midpoint line = <u>2.4</u>cm
parallel side = <u>4.8</u>cm

Practice
1 (see lighter lines, above)
3 Perimeter of small triangle is half the
   perimeter of large triangle.

HCM 16
Refresher and Practice

Square	A	B	C	D	E	F
Length of side in cm	12 cm	8.5 cm	6 cm	4.2 cm	3 cm	2.1 cm
Perimeter in cm	48 cm	34 cm	24 cm	16.8 cm	12 cm	8.4 cm

Practice
2 length of side in cm = 1.5
   perimeter in cm = 6
3 The length of side and perimeter for
   successive squares is halved.
4 perimeter = 1.5 cm

HCM 17
Refresher and Practice
1

Town	miles	×8	÷5	kilometres
Canmore	20	160	32	32
Calgary	85	680	136	136
Lake Louise	35	280	56	56
Radium Hot Springs	90	720	144	144

2

Town	kilometres	÷8	×5	miles
Lake Louise	80	10	50	50
Radium Hot Springs	104	13	65	65
Castle Mountain	110	13.75	68.75	68.75
Banff	136	17	85	85

Practice
1 207.75 miles, 332.4 kilometres

HCM 18
Answers will vary

HCM 19
Answers will vary

HCM 20
Refresher
a

1^2	5^2	7^2	10^2	2^2	9^2	8^2	3^2	10^2	4^2	11^2	6^2	12^2
1	25	49	100	4	81	64	9	100	16	121	36	144

b

16^2	18^2	17^2	20^2	15^2	19^2	14^2	13^2	21^2
256	324	289	400	225	361	196	169	441

Practice
1 a $3^2 + 9 = 18$ **b** $6^2 + 8 = 44$
  c $4^2 + 12 = 28$ **d** $10^2 - 17 = 83$
  e $8^2 + 33 = 97$ **f** $7^2 + 10^2 = 149$
  g $11^2 - 48 = 73$ **h** $5^2 + 17 = 42$
  i $13^2 - 102 = 67$

2 a $3^2 + 5^2 = 34$ **b** $4^2 + 6^2 = 52$
  c $9^2 + 8^2 = 145$ **d** $12^2 + 5^2 = 169$
  e $9^2 - 2^2 = 77$ **f** $7^2 + 10^2 = 149$
  g $11^2 - 6^2 = 85$ **h** $5^2 + 8^2 = 89$
  i $13^2 - 10^2 = 69$

HCM 21
Refresher
1 a $-50 + 25 = -25$ **b** $-45 + 15 = -30$
  c $-99 + 11 = -88$ **d** $-48 + 12 = -36$
  e $-275 + 25 = -250$
2 a $152 - 12 = 140$ **b** $391 - 19 = 372$
  c $684 - 21 = 663$ **d** $395 + 15 = 410$
  e $691 + 11 = 702$
3 a $372 + 12 + 12 = 396$
  b $146 + 11 + 11 = 168$
  c $275 + 25 + 25 = 325$
  d $358 + 19 + 19 = 396$
  e $586 + 21 + 21 = 628$
Practice
2 Multiples of 15 → 45, 60, 75, 90, 105, 120, 135, 150
Multiples of 19 → 38, 57, 76, 95, 114, 133, 152, 171
Multiples of 21 → 63, 84, 105, 126, 147, 168, 189, 210

HCM 22
Answers will vary

Collins Primary Maths

Answers

Homework Copymasters

HCM 23
Refresher

a
×	3	10	6	4	5
5	15	50	30	20	25
4	12	40	24	16	20
7	21	70	42	28	35
6	18	60	36	24	30
9	27	90	54	36	45

b
×	8	6	9	7	2
9	72	54	81	63	18
7	56	42	63	49	14
4	32	24	36	28	8
8	64	48	72	56	16
6	48	36	54	42	12

Practice

1 a $6 \times 7 + 5 + 9 = 56$
 b $3 \times (8 + 4) - 9 = 27$
 c $7 \times 4 + 5 + 8 = 41$
 d $7 \times (4 + 5) + 8 = 71$
 e $(6 \times 6) + (8 \times 6) = 84$
 f $64 \div 8 \times 7 = 56$
 g $100 - (9 \times 8) + 16 = 44$
 h $(56 \div 8) \times 9 = 63$
 i $(7 \times 7) + (9 \times 6) = 103$
 j $(72 \div 8) \times 12 = 108$
 k $48 \div 4 + (7 \times 8) = 68$
 l $24 + (9 \times 9) = 105$
2 a $5 \times 8 + 32 = 72$
 b $5 \times (8 + 32) = 200$
 c $(9 \times 7) + (9 \times 3) = 90$
 d $36 \div 4 \times 8 = 72$
 e $6 \times 8 + 35 = 83$
 f $(48 - 24) \times 5 \times 2 = 240$
 g $3 \times 9 + (6 \times 9) = 81$
 h $(7 \times 8) - (14 + 9) = 33$
 i $49 - (19 + 14) = 16$
 j $54 \div 9 \times 6 = 36$
 k $12 + (4 \times 12) = 60$
 l $16 \times 1 \div 4 + 4 = 8$
m $6 \times 2 \times 3 + 36 = 72$
 n $(4 \times 9) + (2 \times 3) = 42$
 or $(4 \times 9) + (1 \times 6) = 42$
 o $56 \div 8 \times 7 = 49$

HCM 24
Refresher

1 a $36 \times 4 = 120 + 24 = 144$
 b $29 \times 7 = 140 + 63 = 203$
 c $56 \times 5 = 250 + 30 = 280$
 d $48 \times 6 = 240 + 48 = 288$
 e $79 \times 8 = 560 + 72 = 632$
 f $64 \times 9 = 540 + 36 = 576$
2 a $87 \times 6 = 480 + 42 = 522$
 b $48 \times 8 = 320 + 64 = 384$
 c $57 \times 7 = 350 + 49 = 399$
 d $68 \times 9 = 540 + 72 = 612$
 e $74 \times 7 = 490 + 28 = 518$
 f $56 \times 6 = 300 + 36 = 336$

Practice

a
×	12	26	47	63
3	36	78	141	189
4	48	104	188	252
6	72	156	282	378
12	144	312	564	756

b
×	18	43	59	84
5	90	215	295	420
7	126	301	413	588
9	162	387	531	756
4	72	172	236	336

c

×	15	32	56	94
6	90	192	336	564
8	120	256	448	752
4	60	128	224	376
7	105	224	392	658

d

×	17	34	48	75
3	51	102	144	225
9	153	306	432	675
5	85	170	240	375
8	136	272	384	600

HCM 25
Refresher
Answers will vary. Model answers:

a $360 \div 4 = 90$ b $280 \div 7 = 40$
c $480 \div 5 = 96$ d $640 \div 8 = 80$
e $540 \div 9 = 60$ f $285 \div 3 = 95$
g $760 \div 8 = 95$ h $540 \div 6 = 90$

Practice

a
$$4)\overline{356}$$
$$-32 \ (8 \times 4)$$
$$\overline{36}$$
$$-36 \ (9 \times 4)$$
$$\overline{00}$$

Answer = 89

b $263 \div 7 = 37$ r4
c $483 \div 5 = 96$ r3
d $662 \div 8 = 82$ r6
e $574 \div 9 = 63$ r7
f $285 \div 3 = 95$
g $756 \div 8 = 94$ r4
h $526 \div 6 = 87$ r4

HCM 26
Answers will vary

HCM 27
Refresher

a
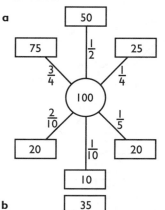

b
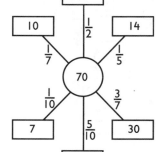

c
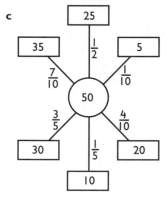

Collins Primary Maths

Practice

d

Diagram (centre **£60**):
- $\frac{3}{4}$ → £45
- $\frac{4}{6}$ → £40
- $\frac{5}{6}$ → £50
- $\frac{5}{12}$ → £25
- $\frac{3}{10}$ → £18
- $\frac{1}{15}$ → £4

e

Diagram (centre **4200**):
- $\frac{3}{4}$ → 3150
- $\frac{2}{5}$ → 1680
- $\frac{2}{3}$ → 2800
- $\frac{3}{7}$ → 1800
- $\frac{4}{10}$ → 1680
- $\frac{56}{100}$ → 2352

f

Diagram (centre **£84**):
- $\frac{2}{5}$ → £33.60
- $\frac{3}{10}$ → £25.20
- $\frac{3}{4}$ → £63
- $\frac{45}{100}$ → £37.80
- $\frac{7}{10}$ → £58.80
- $\frac{5}{6}$ → £70

HCM 28
Refresher

$\frac{7}{10}$	0·2	20%	$\frac{1}{100}$	1%	$\frac{1}{2}$
0·7					0·5
$\frac{1}{10}$					60%
10%					$\frac{9}{10}$
0·25	$\frac{1}{4}$	0·4	40%	0·75	75%

Practice

48%	$\frac{3}{8}$	$37\frac{1}{2}\%$	$\frac{3}{5}$	0·6	75%
$\frac{48}{100}$					$\frac{3}{4}$
$\frac{2}{5}$					$\frac{4}{5}$
0·4					80%
$\frac{1}{3}$	$33\frac{1}{3}\%$	12·5%	0·125	3%	0·3

HCM 29
Open

HCM 30
Open

HCM 31
Refresher and Practice

1

Total	Angles used
180°	90° + 60° + 30°
210°	90° + 60° + 60°
240°	90° + 90° + 60°
270°	90° + 90° + 90°

2

Reflex angle	1st way	2nd way
210°	90° + 60° + 30° + 30°	60° + 60° + 60° + 30°
240°	90° + 60° + 60° + 30°	60° + 60° + 60° + 60°
270°	90° + 90° + 60° + 30°	90° + 60° + 60° + 60°
300°	90° + 90° + 90° + 30°	90° + 90° + 60° + 60°

Practice

1

Reflex angle	1st way	2nd way	3rd way
270°	(2 × 90°) + (3 × 30°)	(4 × 60°) + 30°	(2 × 60°) + (3 × 30°) + 90°
300°	(2 × 90°) + (2 × 30°) + 60°	5 × 60°	(3 × 60°) + 30° + 90°
330°	(3 × 90°) + (2 × 30°)	(4 × 60°) + 90°	(2 × 90°) + (2 × 60°) + 30°

HCM 32
Refresher

1 1 cm², 2 cm², 2 cm², 2.5 cm²
   3 cm², 3 cm², 2 cm², 2 cm²
   $3\frac{1}{2}$ cm², 2 cm², $2\frac{1}{2}$ cm², 3 cm²

Practice

1 a 2 cm²   **b** 1 cm²

c   **d**

area = 2.5 cm²   area = 3.5 cm²

HCM 33
Refresher

1

	Dinosaur	Weight in kilograms	Weight in tonnes to nearest $\frac{1}{10}$ tonne	Weight in tonnes to nearest tonne
A	megalosaurus	900 kg	0.9 t	1 t
B	stegosaurus	1800 kg	1.8 t	2 t
C	allosaurus	2000 kg	2.0 t	2 t
D	iguanodon	4500 kg	4.5 t	5 t
E	triceratops	5400 kg	5.4 t	5 t
F	tyrannosaurus	6400 kg	6.4 t	6 t
G	diplodocus	10 600 kg	10.6 t	11 t

2

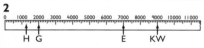

Practice

1 a 4   **b** 10   **c** 5   **d** 5

HCM 34
Refresher and Practice

1 and 2

a 5 g × 9 = 45 g
   5 g × 99 = 495 g
   5 g × 999 = 4995 g
   5 g × 9999 = 49995 g
   5 g × 99999 = 499995 g

b (1 kg + 2 kg) × 9 = 27 kg
   (12 kg + 3 kg) × 9 = 135 kg

(123 kg + 4 kg) × 9 = 1143 kg
(1234 kg + 5 kg) × 9 = 11151 kg
(12345 kg + 6 kg) × 9 = 111159 kg

Practice

a 9 t × 9 = 81 t
   98 t × 9 = 882 t
   987 t × 9 = 8883 t
   9876 t × 9 = 88884 t
   98765 t × 9 = 888885 t

b 12 kg × 99 = 1188 kg
   23 kg × 99 = 2277 kg
   34 kg × 99 = 3366 kg
   45 kg × 99 = 4455 kg
   56 kg × 99 = 5544 kg

c 1 t ÷ 9 = 111.111 kg
   2 t ÷ 9 = 222.222 kg
   3 t ÷ 9 = 333.333 kg
   4 t ÷ 9 = 444.444 kg
   5 t ÷ 9 = 555.555 kg

d 9 g × 9 = 81 g
   99 g × 99 = 9801 g
   999 g × 999 = 998001 g
   9999 g × 9999 = 99980001 g
   99999 g × 99999 = 9999800001 g

HCM 35
Refresher

1 a 10 seconds   **b** 22 seconds
   c 54 seconds
2 a 100 m   **b** 180 m
   c 120 m
3 30 seconds
4 5 seconds
5 180 m

Practice

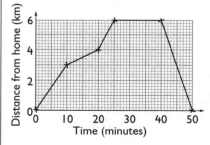

HCM 36
Answers will vary

HCM 37
Answers will vary

HCM 38
Refresher
1 a $0.23 + 4.77 = 5$
b $4.28 + 0.72 = 5$
c $3.14 + 0.86 = 4$
d $2.24 + 0.76 = 3$
e $0.55 + 3.45 = 4$ and $7.48 + 0.52 = 8$
2 a $0.46 + 0.32 = 0.78$
b $0.14 + 0.42 = 0.56$
c $0.55 + 0.31 = 0.86$
d $0.19 + 0.79 = 0.98$
e $0.61 + 0.38 = 0.99$
f $0.89 - 0.55 = 0.34$
g $0.74 - 0.23 = 0.51$
h $0.82 - 0.34 = 0.48$
i $0.92 - 0.71 = 0.21$
j $0.84 - 0.06 = 0.78$
Practice
Answers will vary

HCM 39
Open

HCM 40
Refresher

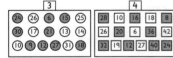

Practice
1, 2 and **3**
a 3: 3, 6, 9, 12, 15, 18, 21,(24) 27, 30
   8: 8, 16,(24) 32, 40, 48, 56, 64, 72, 80
b 4: 4, 8, 12, 16, 20, 24,(28) 32, 36, 40
   7: 7, 14, 21,(28) 35, 42, 49, 56, 63, 70
c 5: 5, 10, 15, 20, 25,(30) 35, 40, 45, 50
   6: 6, 12, 18, 24,(30) 36, 42, 48, 54, 60
d 6: 6, 12,(18) 24, 30,(36) 42, 48,(54) 60
   9: 9,(18) 27,(36) 45,(54) 63, 72, 81, 90
e 3: 3, 6, 9, 12, 15, 18, 21, 24, 27,(30)
   10: 10, 20,(30) 40, 50, 60, 70, 80, 90
f 9: 9, 18, 27,(36) 45, 54, 63,(72) 81, 90
   12: 12, 24,(36) 48, 60,(72) 84, 96, 108, 120

HCM 41
Refresher
Divisible by 2: 180, 272, 3000, 176, 368, 496, 1244
Divisible by 5: 180, 465, 3000, 1625
Divisible by 9: 756, 486, 990, 450, 954, 3060, 324
Divisible by 10: 450, 990, 2100, 3060, 430
Divisible by 3: 1071, 2634, 1032, 1422, 1830, 720
Divisible by 4: 392, 256, 2164, 1032, 4348, 720
Divisible by 4: 600, 780, 3224, 2368, 4152, 1336, 1460, 1072, 2952, 2316
Divisible by 8: 600, 3224, 2368, 4152, 1336, 1072, 2952,
Divisible by 5: 3675, 4290, 720, 385, 265
Divisible by 6: 528, 1056, 4290, 192, 720, 1584, 2688
Divisible by 8: 528, 1056, 192, 720, 1584, 2688
Divisible by 3: 324, 1161, 3726, 4692, 468, 1602, 1152, 5994, 3273
Divisible by 6: 324, 3726, 4692, 468, 1602, 1152, 5994
Divisible by 9: 324, 1161, 3726, 468, 1602, 1152, 5994

Answers

Homework Copymasters

HCM 42
Refresher

a
0 100 300 500 800 1000

b
0 500 1000 1500 1900 2000

c
−20 −17 −10 −5 −10

d
0 0.2 0.5 0.6 0.8 1

Practice

a
0 1000 2500 3000 4000 5000

b
0 2000 4000 6000 7000 8000

c
0 1000 3000 5000 9000 10000

d
−50 −40 −30 −25 −10 0

e
−190 −200 −150 −50 −25 0

f
7.8 7.81 7.83 7.85 7.89 7.9

g
1.6 1.61 1.63 1.65 1.69 1.7

HCM 43
Refresher

a £12.70	**b** £17.50
c £5.70	**d** £1.56
e £6.30	**f** £5.16
g £13.00	**h** £36.70

Practice

a

Buy	2	10	5	100	8
× £1·37	£2.74	£13.70	£6.85	£137	£10.96

b

Buy	6	10	3	7	9
× £48	£288	£480	£144	£336	£432

c

Buy	9	6	2	10	8
× £79	£711	£474	£158	£790	£632

d

Buy	10	2	3	5	100
× £4·68	£46.80	£9.36	£14.04	£23.40	£468

HCM 44
Refresher

Answers will vary. Model answers:

- **a** $219 \times 20 = 4380$
- **b** $320 \times 15 = 4800$
- **c** $227 \times 10 = 2270$
- **d** $300 \times 13 = 3900$
- **e** $172 \times 20 = 3440$
- **f** $300 \times 25 = 7500$
- **g** $250 \times 40 = 10\,000$
- **h** $286 \times 30 = 8580$

Practice

a

×	200	10	9	
20	4000	200	180	4380
3	400	30	27	+ 457
				5037

- **b** $325 \times 15 = 4875$
- **c** $227 \times 12 = 2724$
- **d** $268 \times 13 = 3484$
- **e** $176 \times 18 = 3168$
- **f** $324 \times 25 = 8100$
- **g** $249 \times 38 = 9462$
- **h** $286 \times 27 = 7722$

Collins Primary Maths

HCM 45
Refresher
a $360 \div 12 = 30$
b $480 \div 24 = 20$
c $750 \div 25 = 30$
d $460 \div 23 = 20$
e $390 \div 13 = 30$
f $660 \div 22 = 30$
g $720 \div 36 = 20$
h $540 \div 27 = 20$
i $450 \div 15 = 30$
j $640 \div 16 = 40$
k $840 \div 21 = 40$
l $990 \div 33 = 30$

Practice
a

```
    2 3 ) 8 7 4
      -  6 9 0   (30 × 23)
         1 8 4
      -  1 8 4   (8 × 23)
         0 0 0
```

Answer = 38

b $992 \div 23 \approx 1000 \div 25 = 40$
 $992 \div 23 = 43 \text{ r}3$
c $910 \div 26 \approx 900 \div 25 = 36$
 $910 \div 26 = 35$
d $966 \div 42 \approx 945 \div 45 = 21$
 $966 \div 42 = 23$

HCM 46
Refresher
1 a $120 \div 3 = 40$	b $320 \div 8 = 40$
c $480 \div 6 = 80$	d $720 \div 9 = 80$
e $450 \div 5 = 90$	f $260 \div 13 = 20$
g $320 \div 16 = 20$	h $360 \div 60 = 6$
i $420 \div 70 = 6$	j $500 \div 25 = 20$
k $450 \div 15 = 30$	l $390 \div 13 = 30$
m $420 \div 14 = 30$	n $720 \div 12 = 60$
o $880 \div 11 = 80$	

Practice

a. 3		b. 2	8		c. 1
6	d. 3		e. 2	f. 8	8
g. 5	9	h. 8		i. 2	6
2		j. 6	k. 2	4	
	l. 9		m. 3	7	n. 8
o. 2	1	2	4		8

HCM 47
Open

HCM 48
Refresher
a 2.1	b 6.2
2.13	6.25
2.14	6.27
2.3	6.5
2.31	6.52
2.34	6.57
2.4	6.7
2.41	6.72
2.43	6.75

Practice
a 0.3	b 6.2
0.34	6.28
0.345	6.289
0.35	6.29
0.4	6.298
0.43	6.8
0.435	6.82
0.45	6.829
0.453	6.89
0.5	6.9
0.53	6.92
0.534	6.928
0.54	6.98
0.543	6.982

HCM 49
Refresher
a 20 is 50% of 40
b 5 is 20% of 25
c 4 is 25% of 16
d 6 is 10% of 60
e 3 is 5% of 60
f 9 is 10% of 90
g 27 is 30% of 90
h 12 is 10% of 120
i 48 is 40% of 120
j 9 is 20% of 45

Practice
a 3 is 50% of 6
  3 is 10% of 30
  3 is 1% of 300
  3 is 25% of 12
  3 is 20% of 15
b 4.5 is 50% of 9
  4.5 is 25% of 18
  4.5 is 20% of 22.5
  4.5 is 10% of 45
  4.5 is 1% of 450
c 35 is 1% of 3500
  35 is $33\frac{1}{3}$% of 105
  35 is $12\frac{1}{2}$% of 280
  35 is 20% of 175
  35 is 25% of 140
d 30 is 1% of 3000
  30 is 100% of 30
  30 is $12\frac{1}{2}$% of 240
  30 is $33\frac{1}{3}$% of 90
  30 is 20% of 150
e 2.4 is 50% of 50
  2.4 is 10% of 24
  2.4 is 100% of 2.4
  2.4 is $12\frac{1}{2}$% of 19.2
  2.4 is 20% of 12

HCM 50
Open

HCM 51
Open

HCM 52
Refresher
1

Days	Tally	Frequency	Percentage	Percentage (to the nearest whole number)
0–9	)/ ||	4	6.2	6
10–19	|||| |||| ||	12	18.5	18
20–29	|||| |||| |||| ||||	19	29.2	29
30–39	|||| |||| |||| ||	17	26.2	26
40–49	|||| |||| |||	13	19.9	20
	Total	65		

20–29

2a 16   b 30   c 31

Practice
1 65
2 See table above
3 See table above
4

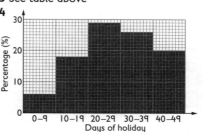

HCM 53
Refresher and Practice
1

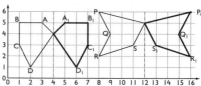

2

Left side		Right side	
vertex	co-ordinates	vertex	co-ordinates
A	(3, 5)	A₁	(5, 5)
B	(1, 5)	B₁	(7, 5)
C	(1, 3)	C₁	(7, 3)
D	(2, 1)	D₁	(6, 1)

Collins Primary Maths

Left side		Right side	
vertex	co-ordinates	vertex	co-ordinates
P	(8, 6)	P₁	(16, 6)
Q	(9, 4)	Q₁	(15, 4)
R	(8, 2)	R₁	(16, 2)
S	(11, 3)	S₁	(13, 3)

Practice

1

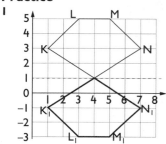

2

Left side		Right side	
vertex	co-ordinates	vertex	co-ordinates
K	(1, 3)	K₁	(1, −1)
L	(3, 5)	L₁	(3, −3)
M	(5, 5)	M₁	(5, −3)
N	(7, 3)	N₁	(7, −1)

HCM 54
Refresher

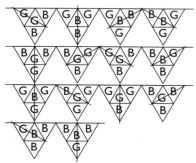

Practice

1

Colours	Number of pieces
2 blue and 2 gold	7
1 blue and 3 gold	3
3 blue and 1 gold	4

2 See answer to Refresher 1 above.

HCM 55
Open

HCM 56
Refresher

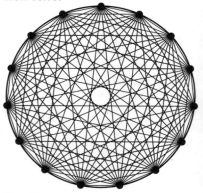

Practice

$15 + 14 + 13 + 12 + 11 + 10 + 9 + 8 + 7 + 6 + 5 + 4 + 3 + 2 + 1 = 120$ lines

HCM 57
Refresher and Practice

1

container	millilitres	centilitres	litres
A	100 ml	10 cl	0.1 l
B	750 ml	75 cl	0.75 l
C	250 ml	25 cl	0.25 l
D	500 ml	50 cl	0.5 l

2

	Amount in E	Containers used	Check
a	1 litre	B and C	750 ml + 250 ml = 1000 ml = 1 l
b	0.350 l	A and C	0.1 l + 0.25 l = 0.35 l
c	0.6 l	A and D	0.1 l + 0.5 l = 0.6 l
d	85 cl	A and B	10 cl + 75 cl = 85 cl
e	1.25 l	B and D	0.75 l + 0.5 l = 1.25 l

Practice
 a 2.5l **b** 2.1l **c** 4.25l **d** 4.25l

HCM 58
Refresher

a
$7 + 8 = 15$
$15 - 7 = 8$

b
$8 + 11 = 19$
$19 - 8 = 11$

c
$8 + 12 = 20$
$20 - 8 = 12$

d
$7 + 6 = 13$
$13 - 7 = 6$

e
$12 + 5 = 17$
$17 - 12 = 5$

f
$8 + 8 = 16$
$16 - 8 = 8$

g
$8 + 6 = 14$
$14 - 8 = 6$

h
$6 + 13 = 19$
$19 - 6 = 13$

Practice
Answers will vary

HCM 59
Answers will vary

HCM 60
Refresher
 a 71, 13 **b** 11, 47, 23
 c 41, 17, 59 **d** 53, 19, 31
 e 29, 37, 43

Practice
1 a $91 = 7 \times 13$ **b** $55 = 5 \times 11$
 c $123 = 3 \times 41$ **d** $95 = 5 \times 19$
 e $57 = 3 \times 19$ **f** $221 = 13 \times 17$
 g $209 = 11 \times 19$ **h** $469 = 67 \times 7$
 i $371 = 53 \times 7$ **j** $485 = 97 \times 5$
2 a $100 - 60 + 3 = 43$
 b $4 \times 25 - 3 = 97$
 c $49 \div 7 \times 1 = 7$
 d $24 \times 3 - 11 = 61$
 e $50 - 40 + 19 = 29$
 f $20 \times 2 - 12 + 1 = 29$
  or $20 + 2 - 12 + 1 = 11$
 g $(25 \times 2) + (3 \times 3) = 59$
 h $(15 \times 3 - 1) \div 4 = 11$

Collins Primary Maths